fertile ground

AN ANTHOLOGY OF SOUTH AUSTRALIAN CREATIVE WRITING

fertile ground

AN ANTHOLOGY OF
SOUTH AUSTRALIAN CREATIVE WRITING

Edited by

Michael Deves, Maureen Sexton and Peter Manthorpe

Flinders Writers
in association with

Wakefield Press

Flinders Writers
in association with
Wakefield Press
Box 2266, Kent Town
South Australia 5071

First published 1998

Cover design Brooke Thomas
Typesetting and production Michael Deves
Printed and bound by Hyde Park Press, Adelaide

National Library of Australia
Cataloguing-in-Publication entry

Fertile ground: an anthology of South Australian creative writing.

ISBN 1 86254 476 X.

1. Australian literature - South Australia. 2. Australian literature -
20th century.
I. Deves, Michael. II. Sexton, Maureen. III. Manthorpe, Peter.

820.8099423

Contents

Acknowledgements

Sponsors

We gratefully acknowledge the generous financial support of

 Flinders University of South Australia,
Office of the Vice-Chancellor

Flinders University English Department

Flinders University Public Relations Department

 Hyde Park Press

 Greg Trott, Wirra Wirra Vineyards

 Imprints Booksellers, Adelaide

 Tatachilla Wines

 ANZ Bank, Flinders University

We also gratefully acknowledge:

The SA Writers' Centre for providing the launch venue.
Lindy Manthorpe for editorial assistance and proof reading.
Members of the group who took responsibility for selecting, editing,
proof reading, raising sponsorship funds, organising the launch and
promoting*Fertile Ground*.

Preface

In March 1998 only one of the writers featured in this book had ever published any creative writing. This anthology grew out of the work produced by members of a creative writing course at Flinders University, and demonstrates how much ready-to-be-tapped potential exists in those who feel the urge to write. On completion of the course a group of these students decided to take the next step and publish our work.

In selecting work for inclusion we wanted to show the broad range of writing styles, rather than simply try to pick 'the best' work for presentation. For similar reasons we have also edited material only lightly, to show the raw potential, rather than offer a slick 'house' style. The result is a collection of stories and poems that demonstrate that everyone has something to offer, and that the human imagination is indeed a fertile source.

The anthology has been wholly produced by members of the group, and while we are grateful for the generous and painstaking guidance of our teachers, for the support of our sponsors, and to Wakefield Press for publishing the book, we are also pleased that all the work of selecting, editing and preparing material for publication, as well as the physical aspects of print preparation, have been done by members of the group.

The two major impulses that drive the writer are the desire to express oneself and the wish to communicate with others. We hope that you will enjoy this collection as it is intended: a desire to communicate our thoughts and feelings, and a joyful fulfilment of the urge to write.

Michael Deves, Maureen Sexton, Peter Manthorpe

For our teachers

Syd Harrex

Rick Hosking

Graham Rowlands

Eva Sallis

Metamorphosis in Suburbia

TONY BUGEJA

I have always felt that I have a special insight into Kafka's *Metamorphosis*. The story of a down-trodden clerk turning into a cockroach reminds me very much of Joe, my father. My father was never a clerk and did not become an insect – he became a rabbit. I suppose it was partly my fault, although my sister must bear some of the blame.

To comprehend my father's metamorphosis you have to understand his past. The place and time that Joe came from did not have adolescence. A person was a child and then became an adult. It happened all of a sudden, usually triggered by some event like getting a job on a fishing boat. Fishing boats are rare in the suburbs and I was enjoying my adolescence. You are probably wondering what this has to do with my father turning into a rabbit. Be patient; explanations take time.

My sister and I were of that first generation to be identified as teenagers. To Joe this was inexplicable, foreign, hostile. The explosion occurred one Sunday lunch – I hated Sunday lunch. My elder sister was going through an existentialist phase. It mainly involved tight black clothing, green fingernails, and nicotine-stained fingers. I was younger; my behaviour was characterised by innocent pleasures like long silences and picking my pimples. Well there we were at the dining room table: Rosita was being existentialist and I was being silent. I will not bore you with the trivia that started it off. There was an hour of rage, three days of hysteria, then he went to the garden shed. He more or less stayed in the garden shed for the next five years. You may think this has nothing to do with turning into a rabbit; I am coming to that.

We had a rabbit called Thumper: it was large and white and lived in the shed. I call Thumper 'it' because I never did learn its gender. The pangs of desire did not seem to affect this creature, although it did have an interesting relationship with the ginger tom from next-door. Sometimes they would be found on summer mornings lying contentedly side-by-side under the lavender bush. This rabbit was of great age. It had been a children's pet until the children had turned their minds to pimples and tight black clothing. Joe took over as rabbit carer, and of course once he became a shed-dweller they spent a lot of time together.

My mother was a woman of funny little phrases. These sayings would often encapsulate a great deal. One afternoon as she watched Joe depart to the shed, after a particularly boring Sunday lunch, she said, 'His face is as long as a fiddle.' It was true, his face had grown longer and narrower. What she meant was that he did not smile, but at that stage we did not make the connection that this was also very characteristic of a rabbit.

My father's hair was turning white, an identical colour to Thumper's. Sometimes, when looking from the kitchen door-way into the shed window, I could see two white heads and could not tell them apart.

I know what you are going to say. 'What about the ears? Everyone knows rabbits have big ears. What about size? Joe must have been larger than a rabbit.' I expect Thumper did have larger ears, but we never saw them. Thumper always had its ears folded back. There was some difference in size, but Joe was a small man and Thumper was a very large rabbit.

I don't think we ever discussed the fact that Joe had become a rabbit – it was silently understood. In Kafka's story the cockroach is neglected and dies. My mother did not let that happen, and Joe was always ready to hop down the garden path for his meals. Rosita married at twenty and I was rarely at home after the age of eighteen. When I finally left home at twenty, Joe was there to farewell me. I don't remember him saying anything. Rabbits are rather silent creatures.

The Storyteller

Tony Bugeja

When I knew Paul I was a very small child and he was an old man. We were both at the age of a profound understanding of simple things. From him I learnt that the best time to pick prickly pear was early in the morning and that boats have souls. When I talked of Paul to others their responses seemed puzzling and contradictory.

The men in the tavern likened him to Odysseus. The priest compared him to one of the thieves at the crucifixion. My grandmother said Paul was really just a rogue and a liar. I now know that all that was said about him was true.

Paul was a rogue, but his criminality pales before the iniquity of the time. Paul, in partnership with his two-masted schooner *Calypso*, was a trader. Men have carried out sea trade from Malta since before the time of Christ, but Paul's trade was highly irregular.

'Irregular trade' could be anything from contraband to stolen goods; sometimes it involved human cargo, and there was always a demand for guns in the Balkans. Paul was not entirely without merit, he was a fine sailor and a good story-teller. But these were the mundane skills expected of a male. It was really his criminality and World War One that made him into Odysseus.

In 1915 the Mediterranean seemed awash with warships. *Calypso* was inspected in every harbour by nosy men in uniform. To make matters worse, Paul's younger brother went insane and eventually killed himself.

Paul accepted the obligations of an older brother and visited his sister-in-law to offer help. She affronted Paul's sense of propriety by refusing assistance.

'Carmen how do you expect to live ?'

'I will make lace,' she said. 'I have some ready for sale.'

'Don't you know there is a war on? No one is going to come to the village to buy your lace.'

'You will take it with you on your next voyage and sell it where you can.'

'I don't sell lace,' he grunted.

'It will only be a package, it won't take up much room. It will be the first legal cargo you have carried in ten years.' Then she slammed the door in his face. Paul scowled at two women slowly sweeping in front of their houses and strode to Johnny's tavern.

'A man is looking for you,' said Johnny as he poured Paul's wine.

'Did he say what he wanted?'

'I think he has something to sell.'

'The second person today – I am not interested. What is it anyway?'

'Ten barrels of Navy rum disappeared from the docks last night.'

Paul looked across the square at a cat stalking a lizard. *The rum will be cheap because the thieves have to get it off their hands. A large army is congregating in Egypt, thirsty men.* The idea of rum stolen from the British being sold back to the British made Paul smile. He gave Johnny a wink.

Paul provided for his family in case the voyage proved to be a long one, and then prepared to sail. Paul was loading water onto *Calypso* when Carmen appeared out of the dusk with a package under her arm. She unfurled the cloth in front of him.

'It is very large,' Paul said. 'I do not recognise the design; it is not traditional.'

'It is six months' work,' she said. 'It is the design a woman makes when she is living with a madman.'

Paul sighed and took the cloth below to the cabin. When he returned Carmen was gone.

Calypso slipped out of harbour in darkness for a rendezvous with ten barrels of rum.

Paul noticed the funnel and smoke on the horizon on the first day out. It was still there on the third morning. He had a hatred of steamboats, especially ones owned by Customs and Excise. Paul had intended to run south once, east of Crete; instead he put *Calypso* on a northerly tack. The Greek islands seemed the only hope of throwing off pursuit.

Paul was navigating the Cyclades when *Calypso* was boarded by the crew of a German gunboat.

'What language do you speak?' Asked the officer in French.

'A little English, a little Italian, a little Arabic, a little French. I am Maltese.'

'You carry a valuable cargo. You have no documents. I think we have caught a queer fish.'

'I am just a poor man engaged in trade. I am only in the Cyclades to avoid the British.'

'You are technically British, I could have you shot as a spy. I will merely take your cargo and sink you.' A sailor emerged from the cabin and produced the lace.

'Is this part of your trade Maltese?' asked the officer.

'Not normally. My sister-in-law makes lace. She is a widow and hopes that I can sell it.'

'The women in my village also make lace,' said the officer as he spread the cloth on the deck. 'This is a strange design, but very clever. I think there will be many widows making lace in Europe. We will just take a barrel of rum. Go on your way Maltese.'

That night *Calypso* lay at sea-anchor north of Andros, and Paul slept on the deck with his knife beside him. His dreams included the sound of creaking cables and English voices. When Paul awoke the voices continued; he was surrounded by a fleet of warships. On the southern horizon was smoke and a forest of funnels and masts.

Paul was preparing to slip away when he saw a cutter approaching. A petty-officer stood on the prow with a pistol in his hand and two of the sailors had rifles raised. *This is a lot of fuss for a bit of rum*, thought Paul. The petty-officer jumped aboard and shouted in English.

'We have commandeered your craft: you are going to the Dardanelles. His Majesty needs shallow-draught vessels for the landing of troops.'

'To Hell with His Majesty! What if I don't want to go?'

'We can lock you up or shoot you. You can complain to the Admiralty after the war.' Paul thought of the nine barrels of Navy rum in the hold and grunted consent.

An hour later three sailors arrived on board with provisions and a red ensign. Paul watched them as they stowed their gear below; he observed their look of wonder as they re-emerged on deck.

Paul gave them a wink. 'If you keep quiet, you can drink all the way to the Dardanelles; if you tell the Navy, the Admiral will drink it all.' The sailors understood and laughed.

Calypso crossed the wide Aegean Sea and Paul watched his profits slipping down men's throats. A sailor called 'Taffy' took an interest in the lace.

'I had an aunt who used to do tatting you know; she always did the same design, it was always daffy-dillies. That lace you have is very strange; it has little white crosses in rows getting smaller and smaller towards a horizon.'

'Good,' said Paul , 'I am glad you can see a pattern in it.' They listened to the thump of shellfire along the peninsula as the fleet waited to rendezvous with the troop ships.

'Very noisy,' said Paul.

'They say if you hear the bang that means it hasn't hit you,' said Taffy.

'Are you going ashore?'

'No I will be staying with the boat. The troops should be

all right. They say the Turks aren't much as soldiers.'

'There could be a lot of them up there. I don't fancy going close inshore.'

'It's a long coast line. They say the Turks won't know where we will land.'

'Never listen to what people say, Taffy, especially "they". "They" are the biggest liars of them all.' Taffy laughed nervously and drank his rum.

Calypso sank lower in the water as a stream of troops clambered onto the deck. Paul cursed His Majesty, cursed the Turks, and muttered a special curse for the soldiers with gold braid on their shoulders. Boats of all kinds were moving towards the dark shore. Shore guns started firing like flowers of light in the darkness. At last *Calypso* was cast off from the troopship. Paul looked at the soldiers. *They are eager. The fools are eager.* Taffy was working the tiller, his face was without expression.

Calypso struck the shore. As troops scrambled into the water the craft gained buoyancy and started to turn as if hungering for the open sea. Paul sighed with relief as Taffy steered the boat back towards the fleet. Neither saw the flowers of light aimed at *Calypso*. The first shell splintered the bow, the second strafed shrapnel across the deck. Paul remembered nothing more.

When Paul awoke his hair was caked with blood, water was lapping over the deck. Taffy lay near the shattered tiller with half his face missing. The sky was black with smoke. In the sea dozens of dead men floated past. *I am in Hell or we are still afloat. It is the rum keeping Calypso above water.* Paul sank back into unconsciousness. *Calypso* drifted on like a grieving god among the slain.

Paul waded onto the island amidst the bleating of goats. *Calypso* lay beached and askew on a sand bar. An elfin girl stared in horror at this hideous man walking towards her and ran away. She returned with a priest and a gaggle of villagers. The priest smiled and pointed towards the Dardanelles. Paul nodded and they led him to the village. I think it was at this point that Paul became Odysseus.

A story was expected of him, but he could not tell of the madness he had witnessed. They wanted the story of a hero in a glorious battle, not a tale of a man engaged in irregular trade. It started modestly enough, the mere telling of how he had outwitted a German battleship among the Cyclades. As repairs on *Calypso* progressed he was forced to tell of how he volunteered for the dangerous task of sailing inshore to deliver the troops. The listeners wanted more. Paul then told the most Homeric tale of all. He told of how in the heat of battle, when *Calypso* was sinking fast, he used barrels of rum to keep the craft afloat.

The whole village was there when Paul was ready to rejoin the repaired *Calypso*. Paul knew that he had an obligation to give something. He offered a barrel of rum and they refused it. Paul offered the only other thing he had, the sea-stained lace. They accepted it and the priest gave Paul a blessing.

When Paul returned home he did a deal with Johnny who sold the rum piecemeal to Saturday night sailors. Some of the money went to Carmen for the lace. He retold the stories to avid listeners and wove into these tales the fable of the lace with the mysterious pattern. The lace took on a prophetic significance and Carmen's work became much in demand for altar cloths.

Paul did not do so well. His enterprises had become common knowledge to the authorities. Paul beached *Calypso* and took the humiliation of working as a deck hand on a Red Sea steamer. In 1918 he heard there was money to be made transporting Russian refugees from Odessa to Athens. Paul refitted *Calypso* and headed once more for The Dardanelles. He was gone for three months and returned with a cargo of ghosts.

The Fall in Naples

TONY BUGEJA

Last year, on a breezy day in Adelaide, I was standing in Rundle Mall with an hour to kill. I bought a peach from a fruit stall and walked through John Martin's to North Terrace. I crossed the road near the Museum and sat on a low wall in the sunshine. As I ate the peach, I remembered.

I was five years old, watching the city of Naples from a ship's rail. My big sister, Rosa, was standing near a group of women soldiers who were yelling encouragement to the sailors lowering the gangway. The ship was carrying a lot of British troops from Malta: the war was over and they were going home. Mummy and I and Rosa were going to England too, and it was going to be home. Mummy said they were only going to stop at Naples for a few hours to pick up some American troops who were going home too. I thought about this. Home seemed to be a very crowded place. An officer walked the deck with his head high and arms swinging; a soldier walked behind him aping the officer's manner. The girls at the rail were giggling with their hands over their mouths. I watched the quay and the warehouses. Crowds of people were buying and selling all along the foreshore.

Near a warehouse, three men grabbed an individual out of the crowd and pushed him against a wall. Then the captured man fell and just lay there like a heap of old clothes. The giggling stopped and a woman soldier with big red lips put her arm around me.

'Don't worry love, he was probably a black marketeer. The

people down there are fighting to stay alive. Money has no value, people are selling their bodies to feed their kids. Thank goodness you don't understand what I'm saying. Go and play with the other children.'

Mummy, Rosa and I went ashore for an hour while the American troops were embarking. Mummy traded a couple of English cigarettes for a large bag of peaches. We three sat on a low wall and gorged ourselves on them. I wondered if Mummy was a black marketeer.

Evita studied their faces as they walked back to the ship. She understood her daughter as if the girl was made of glass, but that son was a mystery bag. He had been merry enough, but had suddenly become as serious as a judge. That boy thinks too much – he was born under a vinegar bottle. They had both been through the war; Rosa had experienced the worst because she was older, but Rosa still laughed. Evita felt that a mother should understand her own son; maybe she was not a good mother. In a week they would be in England, a country where money still had value and it was not necessary to barter. Once the boy understood money he could learn about the things which did not have a price. They had been lucky to get a berth on the ship, what with so many troops going home. She did not think that witnessing the murder this morning had affected him. He was too young to really under-stand death. Rosa had understood, but she just had a little cry and then it was all over.

As we neared the ship, the peach seller called out to Evita.

'Do you want any more peaches my dear? You will need them on the voyage to cheer up the children.'

'No, thank you Señora, they were lovely peaches but they failed to cheer up the bambino.'

'Ah, it is the war my dear, it has been hard on the children. But at least you are together and that is what counts. He will grow old and he will forget.'

She orgasms when she sneezes

She orgasms when she sneezes.
She has no blankets on her bed.
And she welcomes icy breezes!

Through snow-filled winters she freezes,
hopes the cold will go to her head.
She orgasms when she sneezes.

Her delightful garden teases,
flowers in bloom from fence to shed.
And she welcomes icy breezes!

She enjoys her lover's squeezes;
she is allergic to her Fred.
She orgasms when she sneezes.

Through the night as passion seizes,
dust clouds billow around her bed.
And she welcomes icy breezes!

Fred pampers, cuddles and pleases,
now she and he are safely wed.
She orgasms when she sneezes.
And she welcomes icy breezes!

This poem has been written

2000 characters
long for my words to reach them
they align themselves to the page
organise into neat paragraphs
plot against me
march in rows
justify their war of words
the grammar check confirms
there are no passive sentences
6 characters per word
central to the page
they attack
spit themselves at me
i gather them
screw them up
discard them to the bin
this poem has been written

Textually compatible?

Is your program compatible with mine?
I fit your disc into my drive.
My control panel tells me
it cannot convert your file into text.
So what's new?
I never could understand you.

The cock crowed three times

I   I write a Serrano;
drown the image in urine.
It blazes for a moment
then sinks into mud,
buried under wreckage
of glass, metal.
Cast aside,
it is soon forgotten.

II   I write a Christo
a plastic poem
covering all topics.
The tide changes
drowns the metaphor.
Degraded
it disappears.

III   I write a Da Vinci.
My pen points
to the Last Poem
crafted in thirteen lines.
One line betrays me.
For 30 silver pieces
I am reprinted
plagiarised
copied into similes;
not at all like the masterpiece!

A serve of verse

The expectant crowd teases me
with a smattering of applause;
the poem begins.
I focus
and serve my first metaphor –
an ace!
I serve again;
an allusion.
My fore-hand falters,
I lose my point.
My simile slices
the sentence, like a racquet,
a sibilant symbol of success.
Aware of my opponent's weakness,
I send a back-hand of alliteration.
Rhyme and rhythm's retort
to sweat and stress of sport.
Tension builds.
I attack with assonance,
the words bash, dash and smash
their way to victory.
My rhyming couplet
settles the match.
Finally breaking the mould,
the Olympic poet wins gold.

Mt Augustus

You reign over the Gascoyne
in peace
like the Emperor Augustus
ruled Rome.
Your cousin, Ayers Rock,
is the centre of attention
while you stand in grand silence.
Your Horace and Virgil
are the ancients,
Dreamtime storytellers.
Timeless literature,
engravings of the Wadjari people,
decorate your inner walls.
Your name is Burringurrah
 a boy, speared in the leg
hit with a mulgurrah
punished for breaking Law.
Unlike harsh Uluru
you are softened
with grass, shrubby trees.
Your moods blend
from orange to gold
crimson to black.
Burringurrah,
never forgotten.

Fixed souls

Chic to chic, waif-like dolls
are sticking needles in their soles.

With pin-pricks, wounds
that can't be seen
they're shot and fixed
in their deathly dream.
Android creatures
cruise the nights
on catwalks dimmed
with glittered lights.

Chic to chic, waif-like dolls
are sticking needles in their soles.

They fill their bellies
with a lettuce leaf
watered down
with quick relief.
So skinny
they no longer bleed
claiming
fame is all they need.

Chic to chic, waif-like dolls
are sticking needles in their soles.

Those who once loved
rounded hips
now drool over
protruding ribs.
Feeding the hunger
of wealthy passion
starving women
are all the fashion.

At night, she walks

MAUREEN SEXTON

The computer told me the printer was out of paper or not on line, would I like to try again? I said 'okay', but the paper came out blank. I turned the computer and printer off, waited a few minutes and turned them on again. I printed out a story.

The phone rang. It was my mother. She was phoning from interstate. She told me Aunt Lizzie had died. She said 'I am well. You mustn't worry about me.' I told her I wasn't worried. She told me my cousin Rose gave birth to a little girl last week. My mother said she misses me and she loves me. She said to phone her soon.

My mother is always telling me stories. She is a submissive woman. She told me that one night she had an intruder in her house. When she discovered him in her hallway, she felt very angry and yelled, What the hell do you think you're doing? Get out of my house right now.' The intruder was so startled, he left immediately.

We had a ghost living in our house when I was little. His name was George. If anything got lost or broken, we blamed George. Poor George. I felt sorry for him. I still feel guilty.

I read my story. The main character is a woman named Cassandra. Cassandra is lonely. She is a writer. She works all day every day in front of her computer. At night, she walks. Objects are always going missing in her house. She blames it on George, but no-one believes her. They say she is a liar.

Cassandra used to converse with a man named Ashley on the internet. They talked for hours about all kinds of things.

She felt close to him. One day she asked Ashley if they could meet in the flesh. Ashley lived a long distance away, but Cassandra said she could travel there to meet him. To tell the truth, Cassandra was quite excited about meeting Ashley. She hoped they would have sex. Ashley confessed that he is really a woman. Her name is Carla. She is married and has a couple of kids and a husband. Carla suggested that she and Cassandra could still meet and be friends. Cassandra said 'No thanks'. She didn't talk on the internet for a while after that.

I changed Carla's name to Linda. I thought she sounded like a Linda. Not that I've ever known a Linda. Except for one. I had a friend named Linda at school. I used to go ice-skating every Saturday afternoon. I talked Linda into going with me. She'd never been before. She fell over on the ice and broke her arm.

I went for a walk tonight. I went to the shop that's open after midnight. There weren't many people around. I bought myself a chocolate bar and a magazine. When I got home, I read the magazine. There was a story about a man who had always felt like he should have been a woman. So he became a woman. His name is Carla.

I wanted to print an edited copy of my story. The grammar check said I had a lot of passive sentences. The computer got confused and made the command bar disappear. I got angry and turned it off. When I turned it back on again, the command bar was there, but some of the story was missing.

I went to the letter box. There was a letter for me. I read it in front of the computer. It was from Cassandra. She said she wanted to tell me she did meet a man once. His name is George. She had sex with him. He is married to a woman named Linda. She said they met at night, near the shop that was open after midnight. She often bought a magazine to read while she was waiting for him to arrive. One night, he arrived while she was in the middle of reading a very interesting story. She kept reading. When she finished the story, he was gone. She never saw him again.

Linda went to the shop that was open after midnight. She met a woman at the magazine stand. They started talking. They felt like they had known each other for a long time. They felt close. They went for a walk together and shared their stories. They met a couple of nights a week after that. After a year, they stopped seeing each other. The woman's name is Carla.

I phoned my mother. She was pleased to hear from me. While we were talking, I heard a noise in the hallway. I was angry. I yelled: 'What the hell do you think you're doing? Get out of my house right now.' When I went back to the phone, mum asked 'Who was that?' I said 'It was only George.' Later I noticed my story was missing.

Haiku

Writing stories of
a dry, lifeless river bed –
my pen runs out of ink.

Alone in the suburbs
a woman overdoses –
beneath the phone tower.

Sparks from the fireplace
dance to the floor and die –
a falling star.

Acid rain falls
on the grassy meadow –
tears stain my pillow.

Three Days

GAVIN SHAW-ROSS

Nothing really bound us together as friends, except the fact we were both young and sick, we both had to have nasal gastric nutritional support while we slept, and we were most likely going to die. Two guys with tubes up their noses and no futures. We used to share a room a lot; being the same age, they put us together, sharing walls and a television. I watched him one night, during a commercial break, as he fed the plastic tube up into his left nostril, so slow and easy, so natural – like he'd been doing it every night of his life. Then, when everyone's back was turned, I did it myself – independently, for the first time. I felt the flexible tip scrape round the top of my sinus, the metal weights slowly pulling the tube down my throat and into my oesophagus. My fingers, greasy and wet, working hand over hand, threading it in, on my own – no one to counsel or console me any longer. From then on, I'd do it all myself.

Jason and I were friends, by virtue only of the walls and the doctors and the promise of a short future. He had his chest continually beaten and vomited phlegm; my abdomen was continually cut open and stapled back together. We talked a bit and watched TV; and in time went outside the walls and watched the others die around us.

Jason and Danielle weren't quite kids when they met, but they weren't quite adults either. Though they were young in years, nothing in their world allowed them the luxury of youth. The walls and corridors where they first met resonated with echoes – their noses and eyes stung with the harsh cleanliness of the disinfectant-tainted air. They compared the rasping wheezes of their lungs, and fell in love instantly. He was a few years older than she was; she was only thirteen.

When I first met my wife, in one of my university classes, it was so unremarkable that we didn't even speak to each other for the first four months. When I first kissed my wife – though she wasn't my wife then – I knew that she would be. Or I would have known, if I'd thought about it. But I didn't think about it, I only did it.

The exertion of intercourse caused the phlegm from his lungs to loosen and flow up into his throat – it was the best physiotherapy he had ever had. The spluttering coughs; the specimen cup full of phlegm lying on the bedside table that he periodically spat into – these should have been a turn-off, but Danielle simply rolled over and turned her head. It was the only sex she'd ever known.

Two weeks after we got together my wife took me to Prince George, British Columbia, where we made love for three days and ignored her friends. They were very understanding. We played Tic-Tac-Toe on my body – her fingers traced the paths that the knives had left. Driving home, we talked for seven hours about a man she knew who used to abuse little girls, about babies and how I'd probably never father one of my own, about dying and leaving her alone. Two weeks and our lives were planned – we would travel, adopt children nobody wanted, return home. Eventually, I would die and leave her to raise our children alone.

The mucus flow increased, every breath became more difficult. At his twenty-first birthday party Danielle and Jason had to blow out his candles together, in order for them to be blown out at all. The inevitable could no longer be ignored. More and more, the fire and disease within returned him to those walls where his gasps and her tears reverberated through the darkened corridors. He had known what the words 'cystic' and 'fibrosis' meant long before he ever knew how to read them Now, together, they knew that the life they dreamed of but could never have was ending.

There were peanut shells on the floor and the juke-box was bleating out 'Hotel California' when Tamara asked me to marry her. Her pool cue rested against my leg, she smiled and left to take her shot, returning with eyes seeking an answer. I kissed her, buying time, my shocked mind blurred, searching for a response. Her tongue and lips tasted sweet from the beer and the peanuts. She was sure of what I would say, more sure than I was, as my shocked voice squeaked out that yes, I would marry her, but not yet. Yes, but not yet. For once in my life, I had all the time I needed.

There was never any question that Jason and Danielle would one day get married. No proposal ever needed to be given, though one was – with Jason struggling to kneel amidst the crackling of the dry leaves and brown grass of the park near the hospital, and Danielle laughing at the romantic absurdity of his efforts. The leaves on the trees had only just begun to turn yellow and fall to the ground. It was her favourite time of year.

When I asked Tamara to marry me, she was sitting on our battered black couch, and had just got back from working an overnight shift. I began to get down on one knee – she saw it coming and interrupted me to say no. It took me two hours of convincing for her to believe that I truly meant it. The argument lost, she began to cry, threw her arms around me, and said yes.

With slightly trembling hands, Danielle's mother and father wrote their names on a legal document stating that they consented to their daughter being married prior to the official legal age of eighteen. Willingly, at her request, they signed their names, then held her and each other as they all cried. The paper was put away in a safe place, in case it was ever needed.

To love a man who has cancer and will die on you cannot be a real, true love, as it has no permanence. To marry such a man is madness, argued Tamara's mother.

Jason could hardly walk and couldn't stand through the ceremony. Twice his coughing doubled him over and halted the pastor's words. The back garden of the house Danielle had grown up in was crammed with people and chairs and tables with pink-and-white crepe paper bells on top of them. His thin blond curls were slicked back; he wore a baggy knit sweater and black pants. She wore white and carried lilies. Nearly everyone cried, the mothers more than the fathers, the children only when their drinks got spilt and the bride and groom not at all. They returned to their shared apartment – the wheelchair he used in those last weeks was left outside the door as they walked, together, across the threshold as a married couple. The paper had been retrieved from its safe place – it had indeed been needed. She was twenty-two days short of eighteen.

The sun was bright and the sky was cloudless and blue. The kilts and the bagpipes betrayed the Alberta summer, as Tamara walked down the hill in a simple dress of white. Petals from the flowers in her mother's garden were spread before her like tears of pink and gold. With an air of resignation her father gave her away. She was fifteen minutes late – she is almost always late. Our lives together had begun more than a year before – this act was a party to convince everyone, including ourselves, that we believed it.

> For three days of happiness they cooked and burnt things and wandered about naked, watching television and each other, doing all that they ever wanted. At night she held him, listening to the pops and whistles of his pneumonic chest; feeling the rattle in his breathing in the darkness as she stared at the ceiling with tears in her eyes.

For three days we drove through the sunshine in a cherry-red Mustang convertible with the top down. On five separate occasions we sat in line at the Schwartz Bay ferry terminal in Victoria, waiting to go to various different islands we only knew the names of. We made love outdoors and had our first argument as man and wife. It was the honeymoon I had never dreamed of.

> Danielle found Jesus and dragged Jason to him. What other choice did she have, to see him again? Three days or a delayed eternity. Jesus found Jason shaking, feverish and sweating, drowning in his own lungs, but happy, and in love.

At sunset, I watch as a gum tree comes alive – its branches holding at least fifty screeching white cocka-toos, their sulphur crests blazing, their wings beating like drums. Yet still, away from all we have ever known, the familiar fear returns – a bone scan shows the tumour – it is 2.8 cm by 1.9 cm by 4.0 cm, engulfing the left-hand posterior surface of my sternum. Is this what it was last year? Is there any new growth, where none should be? If there is, Tamara calmly states, we go home via Cairns, we do the Great Barrier Reef and Ayers Rock – cramming into a month the memories to last our two lifetimes. No emotion betrays her voice, no burden on me to console her – I both love and hate her stoic nature.

> His coffin was black, and he was dressed in the same clothes he had been married in. She was seventeen and a widow; she had a honeymoon where death was the doorman. At the funeral, she said goodbye to her love, for a time. She was smiling, she always knew it would come – he was her husband and their love would last forever.

I shared a room with him a few months before he died. He looked old and bent. A tiredness I had never seen had grown into his body. He was a man wearing the face of a boy, the flesh of a skeleton and eyes still burning with spirit. Danielle came in, young and blonde-haired, looking delicate and fragile. She leaned over his bed and kissed him on the forehead, her hand resting on his chest, then scolded him for not doing his physiotherapy properly. The three of us talked, we traded phone numbers – she said I should call. She looked lonely, for him and for her. Later, as he slept, she sat on the foot of his bed, watching over him, a girl living a woman's nightmare with the man she loved. At the time, I wished I had what he had. In time, I found it myself.

ages of man

in 1983,
     I rhyme noodle
          with doodle.   my dog,
              a poodle,
        chases a frog
          off a log.
     my third grade teacher,
                  MISS WIGHAM
gives me a sticker of a rabbit and a smile
        meant just for me.

moonlight and music,
seeps into my room.   upstairs
my mother, asleep – she knows nothing of my pain.
she was never sixteen,
     like i am sixteen.   in my corner,
blanket wrapped around me to protect myself from the
cold hand of existence,   i write,
     'dark thoughts, at a dark time, it's a dark age,
     for a dark world – now i am grown, i understand.'
my hand trembling
with the fury of my creative might –
     spewing angst.

In July, I searched the shops of Alice Springs
for my wife's first anniversary present.
I felt the heartbeat
of an infant kangaroo;
I lived a life here in Australia,
that I'd never known except in picture books
and dreams.   I wrote
     about nothing at all.

Good Medicine

The needle in my arm –
          is a dagger in my soul;
          a lifeline to my heart;
          an anchor for my body.
It's the killer of my dreams, the saviour of my future
and perhaps   a phallus –
          to my subconscious.

Miracles flow through it
in both directions –
blood-red life flows out,
the giving of life flows in
          and in the middle
there is death.
The blue network of fibrous cobwebs
tattooing my bone-thin arm
impaled
by the sleek silver shaft
shooting fire through the nerves
of my skin, their axons
winding through my spinal column,
to my brain,   where my voice
                              says 'ouch'.

Disclosure

Within her eyes, those deep brown eyes;
watching miles drive past through light of day.
Darkness brings down its disguise.

A past, where tales of trust were lies,
and friendly hands brought forth dismay.
Within her eyes, those deep brown eyes.

Friend's father; a Daddy, strong and wise,
watched over her, when she came to play.
Darkness brings down its disguise.

Though cloaked with pious Christian's guise,
preyed on innocence thrown in disarray.
Within her eyes, those deep brown eyes.

And placing hands on eight-year-old thighs,
took what he could, and had his way
as darkness brought down its disguise.

Sweetness learns hateful despise,
that later years of trust betray.
Within her eyes, those deep brown eyes.

What does not live, withers and dies,
as secrets shared, once held at bay.
Darkness, as her sole disguise.

Hatred wanes, as woman's soul survives.
yet fear and mistrust still allay
what's within her eyes, those sweet brown eyes
as darkness brings down its disguise.

Lessons

EMMA GRIFFIN

The wind was burning her eyes. They felt dried out and irritated. She reached up to rub them. She rubbed until she saw bright yellow stars behind her lids. The pain was intense and her tears made a squelching noise as they coated the gummy flesh of her eyeball.

A giant paw slapped her hands away and they fell like dead birds into her lap. She did not need to whine and ask why it had been done. He had never offered her any reason.

She tried to resist rubbing her hands or giving any indication of pain. That would only result in a look of disgust and perhaps another slap of twice the strength. She placed her hands under her thighs, where she would not be tempted to do anything distracting with them, and turned to peer out the window.

Red dust trailed behind them in a steady stream. She knew that people on the surrounding properties would be able to see them coming long before they arrived.

The road was corrugated but it seemed almost unnoticeable in the monster truck. The huge side mirror was coated in a film of red dirt and a small spider struggled in the wind to build a web between the support poles. She peered past it to her reflection. It was tiny in the giant mirror, thin, pointy and very sunburnt. Her nose was blistered and peeling, her hair matted with drying sweat and dust.

Without conscious thought her hand crept out from beneath her thigh and reached up to pick the flaking tender skin on her nose. The face in the mirror distorted slightly with the pain and a small bead of blood formed where the skin had lifted. Her other hand crept up to her mouth and she watched her reflection dribble a bead of saliva onto her finger and dab it on the bleeding nose. She hissed in pain as the salty cocktail of spit and sweat touched the wound.

This drew his attention. He punched her sharply in the ribs with his thick calloused knuckles. At once she turned from the mirror and stuck her hands more firmly under her thighs.

She must have drifted off to sleep finally. One minute she was sitting under a bubbling fountain drinking cool refreshing water, the next, rough hands were shaking her awake. Her tongue felt thick and dead in her mouth. She coughed dryly. Even though her eyes were open he slapped her across the face and yelled at her to wake up. His breath was stale and she could smell the hot saliva dripping from his tongue. She sat up as quickly as she could but made no effort to shield her face.

Already he was climbing out of the truck and ambling along the dusty road.

She tried to open her door but her hands had gone numb and her fingers felt fat and unresponsive. She clawed at the door handle, pins and needles beginning to bring her hands alive. She watched her useless fingers fumble with the catch. The handle arced out, then locked and flung back against her stinging fingers. She let out a small shriek, starting to feel panicky, before she realised that the lock was down. Her fingers scrabbled over the hot metal and wrenched it up. Desperately, almost crying with frustration, she yanked the handle again and kicked the heavy door open.

Hot air knocked her back and bit into her red skin. She did an about-face and climbed down onto the step by the door.

The hot, hard road sent spikes of pain up her shins and she stumbled slightly before she ran to his side.

He didn't strike her when at last she caught up with him. She was panting with fear and anticipation. His eyes were focused only on the road. Reaching out, he pulled her shoulder, forcing her into a squatting position with his giant hand.

At once the stench rose to meet her like a faithful dog. She was almost used to it now and knew better than to gag at the smell.

He didn't notice her controlled reaction. He was grinning, sharp teeth poking out from tight, blistered lips. His eyes gleamed, the whites of them veined with red, the flesh underneath sagging in slouching pockets.

The object of his focus was a mangled clump of white bone and ratty tan fur. She could see the thick rotting tail protruding from the splintered remains of a leg. This had once been a kangaroo. To him it didn't matter what it had once been. Now it was simply 'a lesson'.

The eyes had long ago been picked out of their sockets. He poked at the hollows with a thin stick. It made a unpleasant screeching noise as it scraped the bone. He used his heavy work boots to pry the body off the dusty road and flip it over. It rocked slightly on its mangled rib cage and the smell of death became stronger in the burning sun. She heard him murmuring to himself as he turned the carcass again and again. She squatted near his log-sized thigh feeling the sweat collect behind her kneecaps and stomach acid burning in her throat. She moaned softly when she realised the carrion smell made her hungry. She longed for the cool water of her dream.

He turned to her sharply, furious, and grabbed a chunk of her matted hair. He pushed her face to the rotting corpse and ordered her to look. She felt herself shaking with fear. Tears burned in her eyes from trying to swallow bile. The sensation spread to her nose and she could feel a dribble of snot forming on her lips. It was too late to stop now. She knew she would cry.

He shoved her back onto the dusty road, screaming at her in a high pitched howl. He kicked dirt into her stinging throat and the particles lodged there like molten boulders.

She let the tears come now because she knew this was what he had wanted all along. They felt cool on her stinging cheeks and she stuck out her parched tongue to lick the moisture.

The carcass had been flung aside forgotten, his focus once again on her. She watched the dead animal out of the corner of her eye as his fists and giant hoofed feet pounded her further into the road. She was no longer feeling fear or disgust.

She heard a deep growl as the truck's engine started up. She realised it was over; today's lesson was complete. She pushed herself from the road and staggered back to the truck.

He did not look at her as she climbed in. She sat on the seat, ignoring the burning upholstery and stuck her hands under her thighs.

The engine gunned once and they took off in a cloud of red dust. The truck jerked in response to his rage, veering to the left. There was a soft thumping sound as the carcass splintered under the wheels, flinging bits of decaying flesh onto the truck's belly.

Lady Insanity

EMMA GRIFFIN

For months now you have lingered in the corridors, happy just to be there on the scene. You swigged cheap wine and smoked with the others in the foyer. You held loud obnoxious debates. So cocky. So carefree. But tonight your presence in the main ballroom is requested.

Before you can even stub out your cigarette or swallow the last drop of champagne you are yanked roughly down the hall by unseen hands.

You are shoved into a tiny, dark room. You can smell sweat, stale cigarettes and piss. You are in the cloak room.

The darkness is pierced by a shaft of ultra-violet light. You fight to focus as a shape whirrs into the room. You recognise its blurred edges. It is Panic; a nervous, jittery thing. It hops about, dancing and singing as it takes your coat, explaining the rules for this evening's festivities.

Although you are not seeing with your eyes any more it blindfolds you. Instinctively, you reach up to pull it away, but your hands suddenly lack the strength to remove it. You try to run but only end up staggering around in circles. Its laughter vibrates painfully in your ears and you hear yourself begging it to stop. Its fingers poke your eyes through the material. They feel hard and cold. Blackness is replaced by blinding white. Your focus returns. Though you can still feel the scratchy material over your eyes, somehow you can see again.

It hustles you down yet another corridor. The ceiling is high but the passage is claustrophobically narrow. Enormous dark portraits adorn the walls. You want to slow down and look at them but Panic tugs your hand like an impatient child, urging you onward. Your eyes are burning with your new vision. A pain is beginning at your temples. Again you try to stop, try to resist.

It shakes you roughly, gesturing to a set of huge, oak doors. They swing open. You can see only blackness. You are unable to force yourself any further. Growing impatient, Panic kicks you swiftly up the butt and you stumble into the ballroom.

So, let the party begin!

The music for the evening is deafening, roaring silence. The host, it seems, consumes all noise.

Perhaps a drink to settle the nerves?

A crystal goblet is pushed into your trembling hands. It is filled with a black, swirling substance of indeterminate colour. It reminds you of used engine oil. *Salute!*

Swallowing it down you find it tastes hot and acidic, like bile. However, you will find that no matter how much you want to refuse it, you drink the potent brew again and again as the night goes on.

The scent of tonight's feast fills the air. It invades every orifice with its presence, a mixture of the tangy, metallic smell of blood mixed with the damp smell of mould and must: proof that the sun never touches this all night gig.

After a while you feel a numbness overcome you. The drinks are still coming but they start to go down more smoothly. You feel intoxication overwhelming you. Normally you would be glad of this but tonight it only serves to enhance the silence.

It doesn't take long to realise that you are not alone. Your Host, it seems, does not like to party solo. It has many friends. At first you are glad when the whispering starts but soon, when you can hear what's being said, you'll wish for the silence.

Fear is not as horrid as you might expect it to be. In fact

it's a small creature, rather like a sleek cat, only a bit like a reptile at the same time. It sidles up to you, refilling your glass from an enormous crystal decanter. Leaning close to your face it tells you softly, seductively, that this party has no curfew, no finishing time. There is no end to look forward to.

Then it appears to undergo a metamorphosis, slipping out of its scaly, feline body, becoming something else. Before you can begin to beg it to stop, the change is complete.

Terror is far less pleasant in appearance. It doesn't speak as such, but rather hisses at you through its mouth of dripping teeth. Looking into its eyes you lose any power of speech, you can only whimper in a primal tongue.

If you don't vomit, faint, or straight out piss your elegant party pants then perhaps you have drunk enough to go on.

Terror has a hard, shiny exoskeleton and long jointed arms that quiver with restless anticipation. Though it never physically touches you, you can feel its sharp, hairy appendages dancing all over your skin. It seems to reach out and touch inside you. Your nervous system spasms, sending uncontrollable shudders down your melting spine. Just when you feel you can't possibly stop yourself from screaming it shrinks away.

Your Host has finally joined the festivities. It is all around you but cannot be seen. You hear it chink glasses with you and feel it pat you warmly on the back. Though you don't hear it speak, it tells you it has been waiting for you and that it knew you would come. By now you are trying in vain to make excuses to leave. You search your shattered brain for any reason, no matter how inconceivable. Your Host invades every crevice of logical thought. You are filled with it.

Mercifully someone takes your arm and a voice at your ear invites you to dance. Sweeping you into his embrace he twirls you madly about the dance floor in an endless spin. You are exhausted when you finally meet his eye.

Unlike the others, this guest is distinctly human-looking and definitely masculine. He is large and filthy, as though he has rolled in black volcanic mud. His torso is huge and muscular, gleaming with sweat and bristling hair. You know his name but you dare not speak it. He smiles gently as your eyes bulge underneath your blindfold.

He leads you across the floor, dipping you once before snapping you to his chest in a tight, crushing embrace. His breath is warm and fetid on your cheek. His eyes gleam a million colours in the disco lights. He leans in, whispering in your ear, but screaming at the same time. He has only one thing to say but a million ways to say it. You can hear him telling you to bash your head on the floor until you pass out, swallow your tongue until you choke, slit your wrists with your fingernails, chew open an artery. In the end it all means the same thing. There is no hope. There is no point. There is no escape.

Breathless, your head spinning, you fumble through the Foxtrot, the Tango, the Lambada.

After a while his voice starts to lose its rasping edge, becoming warm and smooth, like silken honey dripping into your ears. His words sound familiar and you begin to think of him as an old and trusted friend. This, of course, is where he takes your hand and invites you back to his home.

This evening has been so long and your head is really beginning to hurt. Even though a part of your brain is screaming at you to say no, you find your fingers curling around his in acceptance.

The Belle of the Ball, the final party-goer, arrives just in time to save you. She is the last guest on the list but most assuredly not the least. She pushes aside your dance partner with an abrupt shove from her large hip. You are so grateful you could cry.

She too is human in appearance. Hideous in a bright pink taffeta gown, white stockings clinging to her orange-skin thighs. Red lipstick sparkles wetly on her withered, snake-skin lips. She sees you watching her and does a gross, bulging pirouette towards you. Her arms, fat and cold like dried salami, encircle you. Sausage fingers grasp your cheeks and, inevitably, pinch them. You notice her teeth are chipped and rotten as she dives in for a kiss. She thrusts her cold, meaty tongue deep into your throat, sucking in and breathing out at the same time. At last she withdraws and whispers into your ear, 'I am Lady Insanity and I am here.'

And you embrace this ghastly whore, whatever your sex, because you know she has a carriage waiting outside. You know that even if you never leave the grounds, at least with her there is a chance you may see the sun again.

Sometimes you are lucky and she allows you to return home. Don't be fooled though – she never really leaves you. She is always back to visit. Because, by God, the party must go on, and on, and on.

You needn't worry though – you know who will be there now. You know the rules. All you have to do is turn up.

Remember Number Three

PETER GARNER

It's about time you showed up. Where the hell have you been?

Rubbish! Even a child could have understood my directions. Just stop whingeing and listen.

Yes, I know. I'm busy too, so shut up and we might get away before dark.

Of course it is. I wouldn't have dragged you all the way up here if it wasn't, would I? I have some instructions for you.

There's no need to go all sullen on me.

I'm sure they are, but they'll just have to wait a little longer. This involves them anyway. Now, you know I was the one who released you lot from your bondage?

Oh! That's OK, any time.

No, why should it cost you? Honestly, you're so sceptical. I have some commandments for you.

Well you'll just have to convince them, won't you? They are written on those three tablets.

No, I'm sorry, I haven't seen your glasses. If it's any help, I'll read them to you.

That's OK. Just give me a minute while I lift one up.

Yes, it is a bit. Right, here we go. No. 1, Thou shalt have no other god before me.

Well, I *hoped* you'd say that. No. 2, Thou shalt not make unto thee any graven image.

I'm sorry you should think so because I happen to *like*

archaic language and you have just broken No. 3 by taking my name in vain.

No problemo, just watch it in future. No. 4 means you can have Saturdays off, being Sabbath and all that.

No, I *said* Saturday and I *meant* Saturday. *I* only had one day off so that's all you lot can have.

I can't help that. You'll just have to lump it. Saturday is the seventh day and *that's* the day of rest.

You do that, but tell them I am firm on that one. No. 5, honour thy father and thy mother.

Well I should *hope* so. No. 6, no killing.

I suppose it might be hard to avoid but you can leave that problem to the philosophers.

Oh! They'll be around in 800 years or so, thinking a lot about that sort of thing. No. 7, no adultery.

Hey! Remember No. 3!

Well, I'm sorry you take it like that but that's the way I want it and that's the way it's gonna be.

No, I *won't* allow just three times per lifetime.

Yes, I would be quite happy to talk to your lawyer, but I won't change my mind. No. 8, no stealing.

Yes, I thought so too. I'm glad we can agree on something! No. 9, thou shalt not bear false witness against thy neighbour.

A bit obscure? Do you think so? Yes, I suppose it is a bit, but with you lot I have a feeling it will be necessary. No. 10, no coveting thy neighbour's wife.

No, I must admit I haven't seen her, but remember, these rules apply to everyone. Oh! By the way, you can include everything belonging to your neighbour, right down to his ox and his ass.

No, I wasn't suggesting you went in for that sort of thing. Now Nos. 11 to 15 are sort of connected because I have been concerned for some time about your declining literacy.

Whoops! There goes No. 3 again!

Well you'll just *have* to get used to it won't you? As I was saying, because you lot seem intent on murdering the language, I have decided to make life a little easier for you.

Frankly, I don't see why you should be surprised. I am, after all, a merciful god, am I not? Did I not release you from bondage?

That's perfectly all right. No offence taken. No. 11, thou shalt not use too many adverbs.

Yes, I have noticed you like them and, quite frankly, it is getting to the point of being quite sickly.

Well, in future you will just have to find more colourful verbs. No. 12, thou shalt not use compound verb tenses.

Because they get too hard to say. That letter you sent to the Archangel Gabriel last Thursday had his teeth rattling in his mouth. No. 13, thou shalt not use convoluted subordinate clauses.

Because they make the sentences too long. Poor old Gabriel had to grab for his puffer just trying to read your latest demands for the tribes of Israel. No. 14, thou mayest split infinitives if thou really must.

I thought you'd like that one. We have given up trying to police it. No. 15, the passive voice shall not be used.

Yes I know I just did, smart arse, but that's the last time, all right? Now, just take those three tablets away with you and work on them.

Unfortunately, no, you will just have to manage without a bag.

Same to you, feller. Watch out for that rock!

Holy Moses! Are you OK?

Well no, I must admit you don't look OK.

That's charming, I must say. And please remember No. 3. I see you have managed to save two of the tablets. Which one is broken?

Oh! That'd be right!

Yes, I could I suppose, but they take such a hell of a long time to do and I have quite a bit on at the moment.

Yes, I guess ten is enough to be getting on with. OK, sod

it. Just take those two with you. Someone is bound to get sick of the language being mangled all the time and I know they'll come up with the same solution.

Omniscient? Yes, I suppose I am really. I'll give it about 3,000 years.

Right ho, Mo. You have a nice one too. Shalom.

Tyro's Lament

This writing game is not a piece of cake
And anyone who says it is, is mad.
There must be something stronger I can take
To calm the throbbing in my head 'cause had
I known that something simple, pure and white
As virgin paper could arrest my mind,
I probably would try and keep from sight
All quartos, folios and any kind
Of pen and pencil. Sadly it's too late.
In attempting this most slippery slope,
The die is cast; I must accept my fate
And implore the Muse to give me hope.
I fear the task may drive me round the bend
But I'll put up a fight: right to the end.

The Knowledge Paradox

Knowledge makes a critical demand
On fallow and inactive minds like mine.
The more I know, the less I understand.

Some deep-seated force I can't withstand,
Inevitably leads to my decline.
Knowledge makes a critical demand.

Philosophy and Classics I have scanned,
Empiricists and others I define.
The more I know, the less I understand.

The 'isms' that I come across command
That to each cause I somehow should incline.
Knowledge makes a critical demand.

My reading lists seem devilishly planned,
Confusion is their preconceived design.
The more I know, the less I understand.

I guess one day I'll have it all in hand:
'He did his best' will decorate my shrine.
Knowledge makes a critical demand.
The more I know, the less I understand.

The Ordination

PETER GARNER

Beloved in Christ, let us pray in silence for Evelyn before we ordain and send her forth to the work for which we believe she has been called by the Holy Spirit.

The words echo around the church, forced on by the PA system. Evelyn kneels with head bowed. 'That's me they're talking about.' A faint smile eases her nerves. The minister's words fade into the background until they become a breeze among the tree-tops. She wonders how she has done it. How can she be kneeling here in front of all these people? Is she accepted now? Is she somebody? Somebody who can make a difference? Somebody who can change people's lives? How she wishes she had found that sort of somebody for herself years ago.

Evelyn glared across the table at her sister Maria. She could not take much more of this tormenting from her. It was evil, as if she gained some sort of sexual satisfaction from baiting people. Evelyn's hands curled into fists: she was shaking with anger, ready to strike out, to eclipse once and for all that smug, leering face opposite.

Her shaking hands moved towards the bowl of porridge. She picked it up. Maria's eyes narrowed; her mind seemed to be taking in the situation, weighing up the probabilities. It must have reached a conclusion. Her tongue darted from her mouth, its fiery red tip pointing defiantly at Evelyn. 'Just you dare,' it seemed to say. 'You wouldn't have the nerve.'

The bowl of porridge hit Maria in the face, just above the eyebrow. The leering eyes flashed a moment of shock, of disbelief, then slowly collapsed. Tears welled up and overflowed. They ran down her cheeks and mingled with the streaks of creamy, lumpy porridge. A trickle of pink mixed with the tears as the blood flowed from the cut above her eye. There was a moment of silence before Maria's sobs took control of her body.

Their mother came crashing down the stairs. The dressing gown she had hurriedly thrown on billowed out behind her; her nakedness exposed, a mixture of frustration and anger on her face. At the top of the stairs Evelyn caught a glimpse of a shadow edging forward to see what had caused the interruption. She did not recognise him. Her mother's eyes flashed as they took in the scene. Without any investigation, she grabbed the wooden spoon that was standing in the porridge saucepan. Evelyn made a move around the table to try to escape. But escape was impossible. Her mother grabbed Evelyn by the back of the neck and threw her across the table. She pulled her dress up and pressed down violently on her neck. She ripped down Evelyn's school knickers and laid into her with the spoon. Flecks of porridge flew in all directions. Some landed on Maria's dress but she didn't care. Her eyes were wide, staring with unconcealed delight at her sister's suffering.

Despite the pain and humiliation, Evelyn made no noise beyond a faint hissing of breath each time the spoon descended. All through the ordeal, her eyes remained fixed on her sister's face. Her mind raced between a hatred for those piggy eyes and amusement at the mixture of blood, porridge and tears that framed them.

Now we give you thanks that you have called Evelyn whom we ordain in your name to be a minister of the Word in your church.

The minister's voice brings Evelyn back to the present. She stares intently at his shoes. They are certainly not new but they have a deep shine on them that suggests painstaking polishing. There is a slight smudge of mud at the heel. Evelyn reflects that there hasn't been any rain for a while. Perhaps he has missed that bit. Perhaps he isn't quite perfect after all.

Evelyn could feel the room beginning to sway. This was the second bottle of whisky, or was it the third? In front of her, the mess of playing cards on the small, round table was blurring. Two columns of smoke twisted upwards from the overflowing ashtray. The room was dissolving into an indistinct blue haze.

The two men sitting at the table had gone quiet. Evelyn's groggy mind tried to work out what was going on. She never played cards. She hated playing cards. She used to play with her sister and that was always a torment. Evelyn knew Maria used to cheat because she hated losing. But she loved winning. It was obvious she loved winning! Nothing seemed to give her such an overpowering feeling as beating someone at cards. Or any game for that matter. Evelyn had always been an easy victim.

The two men were becoming impatient. The taller of the two had long, straggly hair that reached down below his shoulder blades. His companion was shorter and fatter, his skin glistening with sweat. His arms and back were covered in tattoos. A long, straggly moustache dangled from each side of his mouth. He turned to his companion and muttered, 'This strip poker crap is all bullshit. We'll be here all night. Let's just get on with it.'

Evelyn was beginning to realise what was happening. She had no idea who this pair were. Nor did she understand how she got here. But then, she had to admit to herself it was not the first time. Where do I find all these creeps, she wondered to herself; where are all the nice men? She felt a tension cutting the air. The two men were slowly moving towards her from either side of the table.

'Sorry guys.' She started to drag herself to her feet. 'Time I was out of here'.

'Like hell, sweetheart.' The long-haired one moved his bristly, pock-marked face nearer.

Evelyn felt two massive hands clamp firmly to the back of her neck. Her skin crawled as two matted, stringy moustache ends slid along her shoulders. She felt his hot lips searching out her neck and his slimy tongue darting out, exploring her skin. She lurched violently but realised she was trapped. The two hands on her neck tightened and pulled her bodily upwards and forwards across the table. The playing cards scattered in all directions. The ashtray crashed to the floor. She could feel her dress dragged viciously up and another pair of hands ripped her pants off and threw them across the room. Evelyn was helpless. The tears would not come. Her eyes stared coldly ahead as her head rocked repeatedly backwards and forwards.

Empower your servant, Evelyn, for the office and work of minister of the Word in the church of God that your people may be strengthened.

Empower. Strength. Evelyn can almost feel the emotion of the congregation as if it is a tangible power slowly controlling her body. A feeling of wonderful calm envelops her. She is conscious of so much love she almost faints. Her mother is dead now and her sister lives on the other side of the world. Maria sent a beautiful letter though, congratulating her and wishing her well. Evelyn's husband and two children sit in the front row. She cannot see them but she knows they are there. They have always been there for her. Sure, her husband doesn't come to church normally and her son doesn't like to be seen there, but her daughter comes – when she can. They are the base-camp from which her journey began and without which she would have failed.

Evelyn woke up screaming. Beads of perspiration trickled down her face. Her pillow was soaked. 'How much longer will these demons from the past haunt me?' she groaned. Her husband's smooth, cool hands gently passed across her face.

She turned towards him and smiled. Across the room, at the half-open bedroom door, two small faces peered in. There was a shocked expression on them. A strange mixture of fear and pity. Evelyn waved to them. They cowered slightly and then edged forward, covering the final two metres in one bound. As they all lay there, hugging and crying, Evelyn knew that the demons would be defeated. She knew what she must do. It was all so clear now.

We declare that Evelyn Rose Swift is now a minister of the Word in the church of God.

A crash of applause jolts Evelyn from her thoughts. She peers through misty eyes at the congregation. 'How can they possibly understand how I feel at this moment?' she thinks. 'I can hardly explain it myself.'

The minister's voice breaks into her thoughts again.

Whom shall I send, and who will go for us?

And Isaiah said, here I am, send me.

An overpowering sense of peace flows through Evelyn's body. Yes, here she is and she has answered the call. But why? Why her? How can she possibly be the one to be called?

All of us are called into ministry.

Some like Evelyn are called to focus on particular tasks.

'So there it is,' she thinks, 'I'm not really that special.' No explanation. No answers. Just a knowledge. A certain knowledge. A direction. What more can she ask? It has been a rocky journey and there is no guarantee it will get any smoother. But she knows that from now on she will never be alone.

I Remember 1957

PEGGY FARROW-BRADLEY

It was early morning, late in the year. Mum looked straight ahead as she drove towards Halbury School along a red dusty track weaving its way between tufts of wild grasses drying off in early summer sun. She knew the road well; she had driven its ten-mile round trip from our mixed farm, 'Newlyn Park', hundreds of times. Our steel-grey Vanguard let in filtered dust, as it usually did when we travelled our local unsealed roads in the mid north of South Australia.

On this particular morning, I recall sitting beside Mum. One of my three older brothers, Warren, was in the back. Mum always concentrated on the road so much, I knew she wouldn't see me sneak a pick at my nose as I hid behind my hair, bending forwards, pretending to look at my list of words. 'H-O-U-S-E', I spelt out loudly, followed by a whole collection of similar sounding words in that day's spelling test. We always had spelling test first thing on Fridays and I loved it. I was in Grade One and found spelling easy.

As we approached school, Mum said sternly, 'Margaret, you have an appointment in Balaklava this morning. We'll just drop Warren at school and go straight there.'

'I don't have a toothache', I replied. The only appointments we'd ever had before in Balaklava were with horrid old Dr Marshman and I hated him. His slow noisy drill hurt dreadfully with no anaesthetic. 'I don't want to go to Balak,' I protested. 'I'll miss my spelling test and I know I'll get ten out of ten because Ian tested me last night and I got them all right,' I whined. 'Why can't I go to the dentist on Monday and miss mental test instead?'

Mum replied, ' It was the only appointment I could get.'

By the time we had completed this argument, Warren had got out at school, slammed the door, and we were moving along the road again. I sulked the whole half an hour it took to get to Balak, playing with my long curls, twirling them in tangles across my face, licking the ends with my tongue, to annoy Mum if she looked my way.

In Balak, Mum parked in front of the hairdresser, about five doors along from nasty Dr Marshman. 'We're going in to see Mrs Simon first,' Mum said. Glad to put off entering the awful antiseptic smelling dentist's surgery, I happily joined her. Mrs Simon smiled sweetly and offered me a seat in front of the mirror. 'Mum is going to talk to her about some Red Cross business,' I thought, lifting myself up into the chair. I imagined my long curly hair styled up into a glorious bun on top of my head – when I was a bit older, of course. I swung my legs back and forth and smiled at myself in the large clear mirror. My brown curls billowed in a mildly rebellious way. I looked about the salon and watched two ladies sitting under big white driers, reading magazines.

I thought for a moment about how Mum and I had been arguing over recent weeks. Arguments about my hair. A couple of months earlier, Mum was mincing lamb shanks with the mincer attachment atop her new electric Mixmaster when she cut off the top of her thumb. She could no longer curl my long hair into its usual six sausage-like ringlets. Every night she would wrap them up in damp rags before I went to bed. In the morning, she unwrapped them, tidied the ends and fixed the front piece up out of my eyes with a neat ribbon bow, always in a colour to match my dress. With Mum's minced thumb securely tied in its own rags, I was enjoying having my naturally curly hair go however it wanted. I couldn't co-ordinate in the mirror to tie a bow, so I would fix the front piece away from my eyes with a small plastic tipped slide, but only until I got inside the school yard. Then I would take the slide out and let my hair hang about my face. Over my wooden desk, scratched and splattered with years of ink in various shades of dark blue and black, I could lose myself behind my hair; it was almost like being in my own secret cave.

Surprised out of my dream, I was suddenly aware of Mum and Mrs Simon standing behind me. 'How much would you like off?' Mrs Simon asked Mum, gathering my locks in her left hand and pulling them back with a wide-toothed comb. She pulled hard and it hurt, almost as much as my pride was beginning to hurt. 'I'm not having my hair cut,' I screamed as loudly as I knew how. 'Yes, you are, Margaret. Now don't embarrass us by making a scene in front of everybody,' Mum spat a loud whisper into my ear, trying to quieten me. Mum was standing behind the chair. She had my wrists held tightly, both my arms were folded against my chest. I was anchored. 'You can't manage to keep it tidy yourself and Dad said he will cut it with his hand shearing blades if I take you home with hair like this,' she went on. I could feel Mrs Simon tugging again. I realised I'd been trapped.

I screamed, yelled and writhed about, trying to get away. It seemed as though I fought for half an hour, but it was probably a few minutes when, my face bright red with fury, I finally accepted that I could not escape. So I cried huge, heaving sobs. My hair was pulled back into a ponytail, tied with a rubber band and cut straight across with a large pair of silver scissors. Still smiling, Mrs Simon placed the long crinkly lock on the counter in front of me, trying to placate my sorrow by informing me that I could keep my curls. I just kept on crying with my head down, as she attempted to cut a style. I squirmed and was unco-operative every time she said, 'Please put your head up.' Any shape would be unacceptable. All I wanted were my long curls rejoined to my head. Mum just glared at me, her arms folded. When Mrs Simon tried to show me the finished result, I refused to look in the mirror.

Bereft of my Sampson-like power, I cried all the way home

and then for several hours. I wanted to be at school. I loved school. But I wouldn't go anywhere with this old-fashioned woman's hair. Looking in the mirror I had seen several neat little rows of 'waves', like the mounds Dad created when he ploughed the hard, dry soil in his paddocks. And ugly little ends stuck straight out the back of my head. Like I'd seen in the *Women's Weekly*, on old women.

On a wet, windy September afternoon in 1997, I was sorting through my deceased mother's papers, old letters, photographs, cards and telegrams. For many months they had sat stuffed in a couple of her old suitcases in my junk room. I found a letter, and immediately recognised it. The writing, in blue biro, is very primitive. It is followed by about twenty X's – kisses. A drawing in red and green of a house and tree fills the lower half of the page. A half-inch section of blue between writing and drawing represents the sky.

I read aloud to myself:

> 16.11.57
> Dear Nanna
> On friday I missed
> spelling test because I went
> to Balaklava to have my
> hair cut.
> love from your grand daughter.

On the other side, in lead pencil it says:

> 16.11.57
> Dear Nanna I amnot happy tobay

Upside down in another corner of the page, also in pencil:

> 16.11.57
> Dear Nanna I am not happy today

I vividly remember the haircut. I was six. I don't remember writing the letter. Finding it forty years later certainly evoked strong memories: the new electric appliances we could finally have many years after our city friends; toaster; stove that didn't need chopped wood; the Sunbeam Mixmaster with mincer attachment of which Mum was so proud. And that shortly after they came to our farmhouse, my lovely long hair was severely cropped.

Suburban Beach

Beneath glorious morning skies,
Walkers, runners and dogs trample trash.
Mentally view the scene under magnification
And you'll see *2020*, the wildest horror movie.

Do others share my anguish?
Is each moment's buzz their only concern?
Corporate subliminal messages
Pumped into walkman-plugged ears,
Drown gentle ancient whispers
Of the wind, sand, and waves,
Every day I hear them saying,
'Allow countless future generations
to know and enjoy me, as you do.'

Haiku

Cars facing runway –
People grounded in the wish
to escape today.

Phone rings in story,
my precious writing space. Love
from ten thousand miles.

One in Seventeen Million

D. STUART GRAVESTOCK

Felix sat in a loading bay of a supermarket, flicking absently at the cigarette in his fingers, waiting for a friend, Matt. A guy walked up to him, a guy he'd seen around the city's places. Felix knew his name. It was Jackson. This guy's reputation preceded him: he was known to be in the right place, right time, and got to hang out with mini-cult-idol rock-stars.

Felix was a little intimidated, the guy towered over him and Felix knew him to be somewhat an extrovert. The guy spoke:

'Hey. You waiting for Matt?'

'Yeah. I'm Felix.'

'Hey. How ya doin'? I'm Jackson.'

'You comin' for coffee with us when Matt gets here?'

'Yeah, why not? I got fuck-all else to do.'

'Cool.'

So they sized each other up and when their mutual friend arrived, they began to interact properly.

But the moment each of them knew the other was cool was when they bumped into someone they knew who was holding a book about the Hollywood Starlets of the Golden Age.

'Oh, Audrey Hepburn. Definitely a fine-looking lady.'

'Indeed, yes.' Felix flipped a few more pages. 'Grace Kelly! Lovely! May she rest in peace.'

'Yeah. She's great.'

This was it. They knew then. They both harboured a love for what they considered Sacred Trivia, of old films, cartoons, and all sorts of what most people considered 'trash'.

Jackson released Felix's suppressed loud-mouthed arrogance, the Spirit of Who-gives-a-fuck. And this they both admired.

Each became the other's double. Spiritual twins. Blood brothers. Best friends.

Both refused to be pigeon-holed into a sub-culture. They hung out together and, soon, they irritated others with their in-jokes, speaking in riddles only they understood. They were by-products of pop culture and lived in the reject bin of the Civilisation Factory. People hated them when they were together. They had too much fun. If one fell, the other would let him, laugh, then help him up.

2

Another day, Felix sat in town at noon, and waited for Jackson to arrive so they could soon run like drugged monkeys through the crowds of city drones. He watched an old man shuffle past in big, dirty, baggy pants and soft shoes. The Old Man knotted his fingers, and stared, entranced in the mesh of his digits, and mumbled loudly. Felix chuckled in admiration of the Old Man's unabashed display of lunacy and decided he wanted to do it too.

Felix spoke out loud, to no-one in particular:

'What compels an individual to share his thoughts with himself in a manner in which displays those thoughts to others? Or do they speak to someone we are unfortunate enough not to see? And have you ever noticed that if you're sitting next to them,' – he turned to an old woman, who had the misfortune to be sitting next to him, and continued his attention-seeking monologue – 'they turn around and start talking to you as if you care?' The Old Woman, who was now in a dizzy-tizzy from Felix's sudden outburst, smiled confusedly back at him, got up and quickly moved away.

Suddenly Felix heard a burst of laughter and clapping. He whirled around to see Jackson, who had been watching Felix's shameless display, and was now almost wetting himself laughing.

'A wonderfully executed masterpiece, my friend! Wonderful! That was fucking excellent!' Felix, modestly proud, gave a little curtsy and greeted Jackson with a hug.

'Right, then,' said Felix. 'Let's run amok.'

3

They bought coffee and doughnuts, and hoped to achieve that magic combination of a sugar-and-caffeine rush. It hit them with its beautiful power. Felix could feel it, all of a sudden, as his muscles turned into one massive machine, arms into pistons, legs into pumps, his heart into one insane motor. His brain controlled it all: one great, stupid, narcotic maelstrom.

They didn't actually have any plans for that day in town, they just hoped that the sugar and caffeine could possibly alter what would otherwise be a boring day, like it usually did.

4

It was one of those days when, to two teenage boys with nothing to do, everything seemed surreally beautiful. A high percentage of the girls they saw were worthy of Jackson's and Felix's approval. The buskers they heard were all of superb quality. The boys strolled along, occasionally spastically dancing to the music that overflowed from the youth fashion stores they passed.

They made fun of passers-by:

'Look! Abe Vigoda!'

'HAHAHAHA!'

'Check it out! That old dude looks like Salvador Dali!'

'Where?'

'There! To your left, now!'

'Where? Oh, fuck! That's fucking scary, man!'

'HAHAHAHA!'

The comparison of innocent bystanders to faces of Jackson's and Felix's culture continued until they turned their attentions to something equally as insignificant.

'Hey, let's go check out the comic stores.'

'Which one? Mario's or Louie's?'

'Mario's, man. It's closer and Louie's a dickhead.'

Mario's was a huge comic store with priceless issues and collector's items everywhere. The people who frequented Mario's often made Felix and Jackson crack up into giggling fits which they had to stifle with their coat sleeves. There were the hard-core fan-boys who collected three editions of everything the comic companies released, and the (very rare) girlfriend who stood behind her boy, bored and disdainfully nodding when he held up the latest edition of *Syntra: The Vampire Queen* or something equally as mindless. There were the young card-collectors, who cared very little for comics and, therefore, were treated with contempt by Mario, because he was a hard-core comic reader who loved his hobby and his job. If a card-collector ever said a word out of line, Mario would make some derogatory comment about that customer's masturbatory habits. This would always raise a chuckle from Felix and Jackson. Felix held less respect for comics than Jackson and always watched his mouth around Mario, just in case he said something that might provoke one of Mario's onslaughts.

When they were in Mario's, Jackson would search for the titles he collected and Felix would flick through the 'alternative' comics. 'Underground shit,' as Mario called them. Although he hated to admit it, Jackson was a fan-boy. He even had a specific way to hold and read comics:

'Rest the spine in your palm and turn the pages by the corners!'

Failure to adhere to Jackson's rules often resulted in a blow to the back of the head.

Jackson had a bag at the store, in which would be put the latest releases of the titles he collected. Jackson paid for half the contents and called to Felix, who was laughing his head off, flicking through a copy of *Erotic Tales*. They said goodbye to Mario and left the store.

<h2 style="text-align:center">5</h2>

'Where to?' asked Felix. He would often let Jackson drag him around town. He didn't have much else to do. But Jackson didn't have any ideas, either. The coffee-and-doughnut effect was wearing off and the city was beginning to look ominous again. They were losing the feeling that they could laugh at anything and destroy any fields of gloom that they came across. They decided to go to the place where no misery can penetrate: The Toy Store. They always went there when they were in town.

It was a massive thing, filled with all kinds of toys, board games, computer games and their most favourite of all: little electronic gadget things. Things that bleeped for no good reason, things that replayed their voice, twice the speed, half the speed and even backwards, toys that roared, toys that said weird military-like things like 'Over the top, men!'. These toys always cracked Felix up into hysterics. He would often sit in the aisles, toy soldier in hand, continuously pressing the buttons to make them talk and then talking along with them. Jackson liked the big foam things that didn't seem to have any particular purpose. Most of all, he liked hitting Felix with them.

There were three teenage girls in the store, who looked to be a few years younger than Jackson and Felix. They ran around, generally causing mischief, much like Jackson and Felix were. The thing that annoyed Felix was that if he, or Jackson, or the girls, were five years old, their behaviour would have been considered normal, but as they were going through or past puberty, people frowned at them. At times he enjoyed it when 'adults' would *tut* and *tsk* at him, and would purposely act like a moron just to rile them.

Jackson and Felix leapt around, having a sword fight with toys that were way too small for their hands. The girls ran around, past and through the boys, wielding other plastic weapons, causing each other minor damage. Felix and Jackson admired the energetic spirit that the girls possessed and laughed when one girl struck her friend a mighty blow with a tiny plastic broad sword. One of the girls took the boys' laughter as permission to interact with them and she snuck up behind Jackson and bashed him over the head with a mini tomahawk. Felix saw this and burst into a fit of laughter. The gall of this girl amazed both him and Jackson. Thankfully, there was no malicious intent in the girl's actions and Jackson knew it. He laughed and then chased her across the store with a gigantic foam snake.

Soon enough, the boys tired of the Toy Store and left to catch the bus to go home.

6

Their homes lay on the same bus route, so when Felix stepped off the bus, Jackson stayed on until he got to his stop. Felix walked to his house. As soon as he stepped through the front door he knew that no-one else was home. He had the house to himself. He loved this. He liked his house-mates but liked it even more when they weren't there. He walked down the hallway, threw his unnecessary clothing onto his bed and wandered into the kitchen. As usual, he had nothing in his part of the fridge, or in the cupboard which was specially allocated to him. The only thing Felix ever had a plentiful stock of was coffee and sugar. If he ever ran out of milk, he stole from his house-mates. This was not because he felt that they 'owed' him in any way, nor was it done out of spite. It was usually just because he was dying for a coffee and he didn't want it black.

Felix made himself a coffee and went to his bedroom, stripped off and put on his dressing gown. This was his time now and no-one could make any comments about what he wore. He put on an old, tattered baseball cap to keep his foppish fringe from getting in his eyes. He looked terrible but, damn, did he feel comfortable. Next to being naked, wearing that dressing gown was the best thing in the world. He took a sip of his coffee; it slid down his throat and made itself comfortable in his belly. He felt like a king.

(Extract from work in progress)

PETER MANTHORPE

Tern

Above the sea
she hovers
motionless in a flurry of motion,
beak dipped for the dive,
watching.

Then, in the missed beat
of a tiny heart,
she falls
leaden
like no feather ought
down and down,
and in a smack of spray
disappears into the sea.

For a moment there is peace above.

Then, wings first,
she finds the air.
She has across her beak
a silver sacrifice
held up to the sun.
Suspended,
glinting,
silently it dies.

She rises
dripping,
slowly lifting,
up across the sea.

Today, in the Mail

Today, in the mail,
a big yellow envelope came
postmarked from your new address.
I tore open the seal
and all the poems I had written to you
sprawled over the bed.

It was a cold moment.

But then
I noticed they were photocopies.
Every one.

Storm in Bass Strait

The wind roars all around. The rigging sings.
The rain is swirling, manic, in our lee.
The spray is everywhere. It flies and clings,
Then flies away again into the sea.
The waves are charging at us, grey and grim.
The ship is labouring from trough to crest.
She climbs, and lifts, and pauses on the rim,
Then dives, and pounds the water with her breast.
And every time she pounds my head gets worse.
It aches. My hands are sweating where I grip.
At every slamming, clanging pitch I curse
This miserable life. This clumsy ship.
Then from astern an albatross glides effortlessly by,
And soars serenely out of sight into the ragged sky.

The Art of Life

PETER MANTHORPE

My friend and I went walking the dog in the cemetery. She pointed out a headstone which said, *She lived only for others.* 'Poor thing,' she said. 'On my grave I want you to write, *She lived all by herself.* What do you want me to write on yours?'

I thought for a while, and then I said, 'Well, only one of us can write on the other's headstone, can't we?'

'Thanks a lot,' she said. 'Cheered me up no end.'

I had sort of forgotten that that was what I was supposed to be doing. We wandered on in silence for a while.

My friend yelled 'Snake! Did you see it?' She ran off towards some bushes and started thrashing around in the foliage. I did not see any snake and frankly I do not think there was one. Neither did the dog. He glanced quizzically back and forth from me to my friend in the bushes.

Finally I said to her, 'Leave the poor thing alone. I'm getting cold. Let's go.'

'But it might bite somebody.'

I was patient. 'Um, the bodies around here are dead already. Can we go now?'

***

My friend and I had known each other for twenty years. Since before she even met the bastard.

***

My friend was going a little bit batty, but I told myself, 'She will get over it.' I thought that if I stopped believing in her, she might stop believing in herself.

***

My friend told me about a dream she had. In the dream her youngest child had died. She was on a bike, holding the dead child and negotiating heavy traffic at the same time. She felt she would be hit by the racing traffic at any moment. She knew she had to ride 30.4 kilometres to get help.

'What sort of help?' I asked.

'I don't know. Just help,' replied my friend in a matter of fact tone. It was only a dream. She told me that every road sign she pedalled past was the same. They all said '30.4 km to Nearest Help.'

***

My friend set fire to her kitchen. She wanted a cuppa, so she filled the plastic electric jug, lit the stove and put the jug on the flame. Then she forgot about her cuppa. She woke from her nap with the flames just about to take hold of the range-hood cupboard. When I arrived she was black and sweating. She had on a pair of his trousers, which she said were the first thing she grabbed when she woke up. I wondered why she would even have kept them; he has been gone for months now. But I did not push the point.

***

My friend flooded her whole house. She decided to change a tap washer because the kitchen tap was dripping. She undid the tap and water gushed out clean over the sink and onto the floor. She had forgotten to turn off the mains. She found she could not put the tap back together because of the water pressure, so she went to go outside and turn it off. It was then she discovered she had dead-locked herself in the house. She told me later she could see her keys on the plastic table outside and that made her start crying. My friend did not want to be laughed at by a plumber who would probably be a man so she rang me up instead. We had a good laugh about the silliness of it, but then she thought about how much new carpets were going to cost.

My friend was terrified. She thought she was losing it. I thought she might be right, not because of the flood but because of how much it scared her. I kept these thoughts to myself.

***

My friend told me about another dream. She dreamt that there was something trying to get into her house. It was almost a man, but it was huge. It had a ring through its nose. She peeked through the curtains and saw the thing running naked around the garden with the rampant genitalia of a bull. She knew she had to kill it. 'It scared the shit out of me,' said my friend, 'but the really terrifying thing about it was that I knew I actually had to *kill* something to survive myself. I didn't know if I could do it.'

'You can do it,' I said.

She asked me to stay with her for a while. She told me she was frightened of doing something stupid.

***

My friend was lonely.

***

My friend had no spare bed, so at bedtime I got in with her. She watched me undress.

'Wish I still had *my* figure,' she said. 'Do you think it's a coincidence that men seem to walk out on you just when your boobs get droopy and your bum spreads out?'

'No,' I said. 'It's much more complicated than that. It's to do with becoming a father. They become jealous of the maturity of their two-year-olds.'

When we had recovered my friend pointed out that we used to think of ourselves as feminists. 'Now we just think of ourselves as women,' she said.

Then there came a great stream of words. 'Feminism hasn't helped us much really, has it? We might feel strong and independent, but we already *were*. Women have been strong and independent for centuries. Millennia. Well before feminism. We've had to be. You *need* to be strong to live in a patriarchy, especially if you're a woman. Feminism's just another example of women doing a whole lot of hard work while men sit around being insecure. I read this thing the other day by an ex-feminist who said that feminism lasted fifteen years and now it's over and the net result of it all is that we are now less attractive to men. Like it was our fault *again*. When are men going to take some responsibility? When are we going to get a masculist movement? When are men going to start burning their blue singlets and their ties and start demanding the right to take part in the really important work in our society – bringing up their own children – instead of banishing themselves to live out their colourless lives in the wilderness of office blocks and oil rigs? Did you ever read *The Drover's Wife* by Lawson? That sort of crap is still going on. He could look after thousands of sheep at a time, but he couldn't take his wife and kids with him. That would have been too hard. He would have had to engage his feelings then. And look his responsibilities in the eye each morning.'

'I'm so glad you're feeling better,' I told my friend.

***

A few nights later my friend woke me up with a terrible racket. I turned on the bedside lamp and she went quiet and sheepish. She had been clubbing the draft excluder with a brolly.

'I thought it was a snake,' she explained.

Male Bonding

PETER MANTHORPE

Hey buddy. How's it going back aft here? How are you feeling? Don't move don't move. I can get around you. Are you OK? No, you don't look it either. Lost a bit of blood by the looks. You're wedged in? You're not going to go for a Burton if we cop another big wave are you? Where's your harness attached? I might just move it up a bit ... there. More secure. I'd give you another cushion if there was one. They're all wet. Nup. You've got the only dry ones. No, that's fine. You need them. No, you need them. Everyone else is OK. No, the only dry part is back here. The rest of the boat is a shambles mate, I tell you. Yep, sleeping bags and all. Now. Let's have a look under that thing. Just peel it back gently. Nice and easy. Nice and easy. Let's see what we've got. Let's see ... Oh, Jesus. Ah ... It's ... It's not too bad. It's not too bad ... really. Let's have another ... Alright. Um ... OK. I'll have to ... I'll have to ... It's going to need stitches mate. No, I'm telling you, it's going to need stitches. It can't *wait*. We're two days from port, minimum. Yeah, we've got some butterfly closures and they're really great, but ... let's have another look. Jesus. No chance old mate. I'll go and get the stuff. Just relax. Yeah, I've done it once before. Nothing to it really. Keep that thing pressed on tight. You comfy? Luxury eh? Right. Wait here. Don't go away.

Couldn't find the antiseptic ... Yeah, I can smell it too. Probably in the bilge with everything else. Oh, the boat's a shit-fight mate, I tell you. You don't want to know about it. I'll give the forceps a wipe over with these little alcohol swabs and that should ... OK. Sorry. I'll spare you the gory details. Won't be long. Oh, about ... About six or eight should do it. I hope. Well, let me put it this way, your hooter's in three bits. Not as pretty as it was, anyway. Where do you expect me to get a *mirror* from? Let's get on with it eh? Here comes another big one. Hang on!

You OK? All secure? Yep. I'll just have to find the stuff again. It all slid down under here somewhere. Just hold that thing over it nice and tight till I'm ready again. OK, here goes. Just peel it back so I can see what I'm doing. No, keep your eyes *closed*. Well it's important that you don't flinch. OK. I'm going to rest my hands on your forehead to steady them, and when the boat decides to stay still for a few seconds ... Yeah that could be days away, right. Here goes ...

Yes, it's in, but it needs to be tighter. Well you don't want the Grand Canyon running down the middle of your nose for the rest of your life do you? Just try to relax. All right mate, I know, but just try. That should do it. OK. That's one. Only about ... five more to go. Close your *eyes*. OK. Here goes again ... Right, just going to tighten ... Oh, shit shit shit here comes another ... Hang on!

You OK? Yeah don't worry about me, I'm all right, but all the gear has gone schooner-rigged across the deck again. And, ah, the bad news is that that last one pulled out. Just have to do it again. Hang on till I get my shit together. Right, here goes. I'll try to get it back through the same holes, and it might not hurt. Funny you should mention it, but a big fat sow just winged it past the port hole as you spoke. How spooky is that? OK. Try and laugh with your mouth closed; you're opening up the wound. Here goes ...

Right, that's two. How are you feeling? Apart from sore? Yeah, I'm not feeling too flash either. I'm going to get a bucket just in case.

Right. Number three needs to go in about ... Sorry. I'll

just shut up and do it. Here comes another big one! Hang on!

You OK? Right. Let's get on with it. Close your *eyes*. Here goes ...

Sorry mate. I'm really sorry, but I have to pull them tight. If I don't do this properly ... Well, have you ever seen a chick-magnet with three noses? Right, well let's get on with it then. Here goes ...

Hang in there mate. You're a champion. Won't be long now. Can you just wipe away that ... stuff ... under your nose there ... with the ... thing? It's pretty ropy, but finding a clean rag on this boat right now ... Let's just get on with it eh? OK. Here goes ...

Right. Well, I'm happy to report that you're back to having a single proboscis old chap. But there's still a slight problem with the nostrils. Ah, you've only got one. They sort of join up. Um, the bit of skin between them is split. Well, you're going to look like Yoda if I don't. Just one more mate. Hang in there. Holy snapping duck-shit here comes another big one. Hang on!

Just collecting the stuff. Won't be a moment. OK. Here goes ... Here goes ... Well it's taking so long because I've sort of got the shakes a little bit, and there's not much room for error on this bit. Just relax. *Try* to relax then. Here goes ...

Whoa! Sorry about that one. It just kept going in and in and in. Didn't want to turn around and come back out again. I bet it did. My eyes are watering too mate, don't worry. It comes out sort of half way down to your top lip. Would you like me to do it over again? Didn't think so. No, I'm not finished yet. I have to pull it tight ... Nowhere near closed up yet, mate, sorry ... Still wide open. I've got to give it another yank. Hang in there ... Still a bit more to go ... I can't leave it like that, mate, honestly. Just bear with me. Close your eyes and relax. Here goes ... Ah, one more tug should close it up. Mate, this is hurting me too, believe me. Just hang in there a little bit longer. We're nearly done. Here we go ...

That's it mate. We're done. You're a hero. No anaesthetic. Oh, you look absolutely gorgeous again, don't worry. The last time? Ah, well, I've got a little confession to make. Nup. Never. So I lied to you. I thought you might have got nervous or something. Um, could we talk about this later? I think I need some air.

Haiku

Blank and wintry page.
But is that the distant sound
Of a spring of ink?

I can hear the stream
Of traffic from my terrace.
Soon I must dive in.

The wood shed roof sags.
My hammer lying idle –
Time is running out.

BROOKE THOMAS

My Siren Song

I have decided to become a Siren
I will run to the water, tear off my clothes, let my hair
  blow wild in the ocean gales
I am tired of gentleness
I am tired of coyness
I will run into the cold embrace of the sea
and she will thunder her welcome to another of
  Aphrodite's sisters
my return to the waters of my birth
the waters of ambition and of destruction

I do not want to sing melodiously and let my voice
  float on the breeze
I want to scream with abandon and hear my voice
  above the roaring tempest
I want to serenade you into complacency
seduce you into vulnerability
and when you are helpless with desire
I will lure you onto the rocks and laugh with cruel
  rapture
to see your body pierced and battered
pounded and tossed

I will command the waves that hurl you
they will sweep you to the shore, let you draw one
  hopeful breath
then drag you back into the depths
I will throw my head back and scream my ecstasy to
  thunderous skies
as you are sucked down into the endless green
bruised and bleeding

Let me look into your eyes
They are wide and desperate, yet I will feel no pity
  toward you
Fool, you deserve this fate
Did you think I would leave you unscathed?

Hibiscus

Everyday I walk past his house and I am tempted.
In the front garden, a spindly hibiscus tree extends
towards me a slender stem bearing a single blood-red
bloom: five wrinkled scarlet petals encircling the
stamen that shudders in the breeze.

  I think about him all day and every day when I reach
the corner of his street, my breath quickens and my
pace slows. *Will I or won't I? Should I or shouldn't I?* If I
pause to pluck the flower I must lean over the hedge.
If I stretch over the hedge my hand may come to rest
on the gate. If I rest on the gate I might find myself
opening it. When I open the gate, I will go in to him,
bearing the flower like a gift.

  He will unlock the door, I will give him the flower.

  He will embrace me and the crushed petals will fall
to the floor, soft crimson confetti.

The Company Jetty

BROOKE THOMAS

Justine you are a silly cow. Oh hell, did I just say that out loud? The bartender is looking at me strangely so I must've. Oh God, now I'm talking to myself! Oh shit, I just said 'Oh God'! Oh God, I did it again! Justine, calm down, take a few deep breaths and have another drink. Shit, that makes three before the date even starts. I'm gonna be pissed before he gets here at this rate and then there'll be no hope for me. I always was a sucker for a good margarita. Well, at least I can't be held responsible for my actions once I've had a few. Yeah, but who's going to be impressed if I fall off my chair or stagger on my way to the salad bar? I've gotta get my act together before he arrives. Why on earth did I say yes to a Mexican restaurant? The evening starts out well but before you know it your taco implodes or the bottom falls out of your enchilada and you've got salsa running down your chin and guacamole in your lap. Then you've lost every hope of looking sophisticated. Must remember to pick something dainty and easy to eat. What on earth am I doing here?

Where in hell is he anyway? Either I'm early or he's late but I don't know 'cause my watch is at home on top of the fridge which is probably where I left my brain this morning otherwise I wouldn't have said I'd go out with Eric. Why does that guy behind the bar keep looking at me? Sitting here all dressed up and drinking alone I must look like I've been stood up. That, or I just look like a prostitute. Damn it, I knew this dress was too short! What was I thinking? Torn between sexy-confident and sweet-demure and facing a wardrobe bursting with nice gear, I had to pick the most tarty outfit! Well who was I kidding about sweet-demure? God knows that's an act that lasts about two minutes with me before I say something stupid or laugh raucously or belch unexpectedly or slip over and flash my knickers accidentally. Trying to be elegant never works – I'm just too damn loud and open to suggestion after a couple of drinks. Must try to laugh without cackling and not reveal too much personal information on the first date – or at least in the first hour! Stop looking at me, damn it! Maybe he just thinks I'm cute. Come to think of it, he's rather good-looking. Yep, if I just scull down this one, I'll get him over here to get me another. Actually, no, it must be because I look like a hooker. Oh what the hell! Apparently either way I've got him interested.

Still no sign of Eric. Hell, if there's one thing worse than being stood up on a date, it's being stood up by a married man on a date. How low can you go? Of course, that's a question for later, we haven't even had dinner yet! Oh dear – giggling fit – now not only do I look like I've been stood up but I must also look like a complete nutcase. I think I'm nervous. That or very hungry because my stomach's turning somersaults. Why should I be nervous? After all, I've been on enough first dates, it's just that not many of them lead to anything long-term. Then why on earth am I about to have dinner with a married man? Well, of course I know it's not going much further than the back seat of his car or a room in the nearest motel, but God, I mean Jeez, I mean, well – he's so gorgeous! Bright blue eyes that smile all on their own, that thick dark hair, that deep sexy voice, oh and a bum like two peaches in a silk handkerchief. Hey that's a good one, must remember to use it again sometime. Of course, I s'pose he never would have made a move on me if I wasn't such a compulsive flirt. I wonder if I could even have a normal conversation with a bloke without resorting to eyelash batting and giggly innuendo? Oh sure it helped me with the boss – I got a new desk, not to mention a raise, but I really must learn to draw the line somewhere. How does the old workplace slogan go? *No fishing off the company jetty*. There's something called sending the 'wrong signals' and I seem to have a natural flair for it.

Oh why in hell do I care if I impress this guy anyway? Maybe now I'm just curious. First it was, *Oh Justine, you have such beautiful hair* and *Hi Gorgeous, what time's your coffee break?* Then there was *Why don't you join me and some of the guys for a drink after work?* which suddenly turned into *Oh yeah, the guys couldn't come so why don't we make it dinner – just the two of us?* I'm not completely stupid – I can see what's happening. No, I am stupid – if I was smart I wouldn't have said yes, which is why I'm here in this wretched restaurant with fake cactuses … cacti … whatever, and stupid big straw hats on the walls. And I just hate those fake piñata things hanging from the ceiling – the urge to take a long stick and belt the hell out of them is just too much. Oh God I need another drink!

Where the hell is he? I keep going to look pointedly at my watch just to prove to the bartender that I am actually waiting to meet someone and I'm not a total desperado. Maybe he's not coming after all. I should leave now while I still can … Uh oh, too late – there he is, standing in the doorway looking for me. Would it be too obvious if I got down on all fours and crawled behind the bar and out the back? Then the bartender would definitely think I was weird … or drunk … or desperate. And everybody would see my knickers because of this stupid dress. Too late, he's seen me – he's walking over. Damn it, he's so gorgeous – it's not fair. What chance do I stand? Somebody else is gonna be seeing my knickers shortly if I don't regain some composure and self-control. Remember – don't laugh too loud, don't belch, don't order tacos, don't have too much to drink, don't stand up too quickly … well, here he is.

Well, hello. Yeah I'm fine. Thanks, I hoped you'd like it. Yes, I love Mexican food. No, I haven't been waiting long. Yes, I'd love another drink …

Cash Flow

BROOKE THOMAS

The door to the room was heavy and locked. Through the one tiny window you could see a petite, brown-haired woman seated at a wide desk, head bent, hands busy, intent on her task …

Penny sat with her back to the door. The notes flew through her hands; *bruised monarchs, rusty heroines, cobalt legends*. Counting off the notes, fanning them out from her left hand into her right, she formed piles of hundred dollar lots; *one hundred, two fifties, five twenties*. Her hands had come to function of their own accord and with a constant fascination for their speedy, effortless work, she watched the notes spread out across the desk like a picnic rug. She never *counted*, so much as *sensed* each note, its value transmitted to her through its minute textures; fine chiaroscuro and tiny cross-hatching. The process came to her as naturally as breathing.

Her eager hand dived into each canvas bag, bringing up clutches of notes in colourful profusion, like a bunch of brilliant flowers; *cornflower blue, rose, leaf-green*. As she peeled notes deftly away from the haphazard bundle in her left hand, transferring them to ordered piles on the desk, she could sense an upside-down note with her fingertips almost before she saw it. It was as if her hands possessed their own vision. She flipped the errant notes over dexterously, the money fluttering through her long fingers, whispering like doves' wings; *purple, gold, azure*. Before snatching each note, she dragged her left thumbnail swiftly down its centre to make sure it was separated from its fellows. The sound was like whistling wind or the sharp intake of breath. In bundles of ten, she folded the notes over on themselves and listened for the satisfying crack as she snapped a rubber band around them. She repeated this until she had ten times ten notes, folded bundles back to back, crossed each way with double-wrapped rubber bands. Her fingers knew the routine instinctively. She mustered the notes into bright regimental rows and returned them to the vault where the coin rolls stood to attention, stiff green and brown sentinels. Their less ordered fellows jangled heavily in leather bags waiting for Penny's commanding hands.

She loved the metallic sounds as she sorted coin. The harsh grate on the table of a heavy fifty-cent piece, the corrugated glide of a twenty, the smooth golden slide of a dollar coin. She flicked each coin with the tip of her right index finger, shooting it over the edge of the table to where her cupped left hand waited. She possessed unfailing aim; the coins dropped in with a clean silvery *clink* until there were ten of them in the palm of her hand. The metal was cool on her skin, as she raised her index and ring fingers so that the coins fell into a neat line along her middle finger. Then she scooped them up swiftly and onto the desktop, pushing the stack out onto the table with her middle knuckle, forming neat stacks of ten, five and two dollar lots. As she worked, mesmerised by the fleet flow of brass and nickel under her fingers, piles of coin grew up along the desk, metallic stalagmites void of their descending partners. Then, encircling each small tower with her fingers, she swept them by pairs into new plastic bags.

When Penny twirled the combination lock of the safe it was like a dance with precise steps. As she spun the dial through the sequence of numbers, she listened for the secret clunks coming from deep within the thick metal. She had to wrench the door open with all the effort her small frame could summon, but when the great solid slab of iron had gathered its own momentum, it took all her weight to stop it swinging too wide. When she closed the door, she braced one foot against it to stop it bouncing as the connecting surfaces sounded a deep, ominous, prison-door *clang*. When she opened the heavy vault door, the escaping air was stale, bearing the acrid odour of iron and the silvery scent of coins. The smell was like the taste of blood. It would hang about her hair and clothes for hours, long after she had locked down the vaults for the night. It was the smell of a thousand hands and pockets and leather wallets; of exchanges between customer and teller, investor and banker, parent and child. Penny was not afraid to gather all this history up into her soft, sensitive hands and guide each note, with its vast and untraceable past, into neatly ordered bundles. Here among the whispers and clinks of money being sorted she commanded notes and coins with her all-seeing hands; she sensed with her skin, she heard through her fingertips.

Penny did not hear the blast as the door behind her was blown away. Hard metal lodged in her back, her chest crushed against the desk. She gasped for breath. Blackness closed in upon her like the slamming of the vault. She tasted metal, warm, red and ferrous. She heard only the heavy gushing as piles of coins came crashing down to the floor with her, a silver and gold cascade, cool as water, hard as ice. And with the vision in her hands, she saw the notes fly up like startled parrots, fluttering wings of scarlet, emerald and blue. They rose up and spread out, swirling against the white ceiling, outraged at chaos, wild with liberation. A rampant rainbow of history, a flooding torrent of currency, the money descended and scattered over the floor, spreading over her crumpled body like a funeral cloak.

Haiku

The sun is setting
Gold orb dangling over sea –
God bobs for apples.

COCONUTS

Coconuts *(Feast tomorrow)*
Towering high, obscuring the horizon,
slender trunks flank the crushed coral road.
The coconut trees fling green-fronded arms
into the blue of the tropical sun.
The men labour under the harvest load
of kumala, hopa and taro palm.

Coconut Palms *(Harvesting)*
On the plantations in the midday heat
children laugh and climb among the palm crowns.
They toss the coconuts down amongst the trees
to where the men lie asleep at their feet.
The children's bodies are shiny and brown
They slide down the trunks and grip with their knees.

Coconut Baskets *(Flirting)*
Young men scale the trees, knives held in their teeth;
Rusty blades slice and the palm leaves rain down.
The girls gather them and sit in the shade.
Braiding each leaf into a giant wreath,
they weave the fronds as the boys laugh and call,
then run back home with the baskets they've made.

Coconut Cream *(Cooking)*
The men sharpen stakes as the women wait;
The children bring the coconuts in teams;
Then with three expert cracks each nut is husked.
The women all sing as they scrape and grate
the white flesh to make the rich coconut cream.
The flight of the sacred fox signals the dusk.

Coconut Crabs (*Hunting*)
The men wait amongst the palms at twilight
for the coconut crabs to emerge from the sand
– hard-shelled grey bodies waving one giant claw;
They must be grabbed quickly, their pincers bound tight
– those claws have been known to crush a man's hand.
The men return as dawn creeps up the shore.

Coconut Oil (*Dancing*)
The girls prepare to dance for the king.
Swathed in tapa and crowned with frangipani,
anointed with coconut oil their brown skins glow,
their hands tell a story as the women sing.
And the watching assembled company
Give money as thanks for their graceful show

Coconut Bowls (*Talking*)
The men retire and the ritual begins
Kava is brewed in the giant carved bowl.
The host fills up the half-coconut shell.
Each man speaks his turn when the cup comes to him;
the cup passes on and stories are told
weaving the magic of an ancient spell.

Coconut Shells (*Playing*)
When all the feasting and dancing is done
the boys take off their shoes and run to the sea.
At the blow holes they throw down coconut shells
and by the orange light of the setting sun
waves hurl the shells up; the boys laugh with glee.
They run lightly along the reef as waves swell.

Black Veins

Kristy Rebbeck

I have Hepatitis C. I am going to die of liver failure. I'm OK now, but I'm gonna die young and it's gonna be painful. I'm gonna be really sick when I come off this. More sick than you have ever felt in all your entire life. Look at this. I am not ashamed of these, but you know, there's a stigma attached to track marks, so I can't wear short tops in public. Some of these are OK, but see this one, its all scar tissue now, so it'll never heal. See how I've followed the vein up, they actually look OK there. Do you know that when a user dies their veins go black? They have to use heaps of make up to cover them. People will think I'm a bit weird – you know, a corpse with strange coloured arms and stuff. Guess it won't matter when I'm dead, hey?

Now you can do it once, and that's all right, but you've gotta promise me that you'll never do it again, OK. Do you still wanna do it? I'll understand if you don't. See, the thing is, I've been cutting down for ages now, I haven't had any for a while, but I need to have some first so I know what it's like. When I come down I'm gonna be so ill. But I need to try it first. They put heaps of shit in it here. I mean it's pretty heavy gear that I get at The Cross. It's probably different for you. I've heard you mostly get pure gear in Adelaide. You just gotta be careful – you know they put all sorts in it sometimes: speed, cocaine, you just gotta be careful. Do you still wanna do it?

One for you. Your very own. Tungsten steel, only the

finest. You can open the packet, just don't take off the cover yet. Yep, the orange plastic thing – or else you might infect the needle or something. Don't worry, I'm being heaps careful. We need to close the windows, or else it'll blow everywhere. I've done that before. Also, we need some water, something sterile. Got any bottled water? Tap water will do. I should've been more prepared and boiled some. Doesn't matter, I've started now. You're gonna have to shut that more. Yeah, that's OK, I've just gotta check it. Shit that stuff tastes disgusting. It's just like oil. Yeah, it's supposed to – it'll be good stuff.

The spoon? Yeah, it's plastic. Bit different from *Trainspotting*! I mean obviously I can't get out my lighter and try and heat it or anything. But you don't need to boil the water. The gear that you get here is from Asia, I think, and the stuff in the UK is from somewhere like South America. Australian stuff is white, and in the UK it's brown. This dissolves in water really easily, so you don't have to heat it. It's pretty handy actually. No mess, no fuss. You know they actually give you spoons in the needle exchanges here, and some places give you water too. I was pretty impressed; they don't do that at home. Do you still wanna do it?

I'll do mine first. It's OK, nothing will touch me and then touch the spoon. I'm really careful about that sort of thing. I only withdraw about 15 mils of water. I'll do the same for you. I'm not giving myself much tonight. You won't need much and I don't wanna give you too much. Just enough to make you happy and not enough to make you pass out. You probably won't get a massive rush – not on your first time. I can't say exactly how you'll react. That was a long time ago. I did it myself and I just crashed. I think I had too much then, so I don't wanna do the same with you. Also I don't wanna be up for murder.

Can you pass me some of that cotton wool. You only need a little bit. Well, it stops any big bits getting in the syringe. A piece that big – no that little one – yeah, a bit like that is enough to give you a massive heart attack. We have to make sure all of it is dissolved and there aren't any hard bits. Do you still wanna do it? That looks OK to me. I've gotta get more air out. Have you heard that thing that if someone injects air into your blood you'll die? Well, I need a bit in here or else I can't inject it the full way. I don't like to have too much though – yeah, that'll do. Have you got a tie or something? I probably should use a tourniquet just to show you the right way. Yeah, that'll be good. Nah, I don't normally use one, that's why some of my scars are worse. See, I only have to pump my hand a little bit and it comes up really well. Do you know why we use a vein and not an artery? It's gotta be a vein 'cause the arteries pump blood to your brain and the veins pump it away and we definitely don't want this shit going straight to your brain. The arteries are huge – that's a vein there. Do you still wanna do it? No, this won't make me pass out – it'll just make me feel normal again. Funny, hey? See, I only have to pull back a little. Yeah, that's blood. You only have to do it slowly. No, I won't feel it until I take this tie off, then my blood will start pumping again. Can you just loosen that now. Yeah, I can feel it. Oh I'm OK. Hang on a sec ...

I just need some time ...

let it into you – pure and beautiful – unnerving to the end – wired – wired – wiring – into your wires – your electric blue wires – charging your arm – from tip to tip – extinguish your pain – takes the pain – removes – it takes as much as it gives –

you're not alone – sensing she's in the room – fuck you're not alone – you will never be alone – always filled to the brim – completely

a challenge to return – it's all gone now – disappearing into the light – the pure light of day – balloons filled with light

into your soul – penetrate its life – still there watching you – nowhere to hide – you can't ever escape – from here to there

she's looking into you – pulling at flesh – stripping your skeleton – a string of tales without an end – typical

shake your head – shake your head.....

Can you just check my pupils? Yeah, they get really tiny. Good, it means it's working. Once my pupils went so tiny, just like pin pricks. Really weird; I looked like a full-on freak. OK, you'll need about this much. Do you still wanna do it? You'll probably vomit you know. I mean you *will* vomit, you'll vomit heaps. Have you eaten? Make sure you drink heaps of water now then. You know, a few times that I've been here I've got past that door and had to run so fast to get to the toilet. Now you know why users get so skinny: anything you eat comes straight back up again. But it doesn't hurt at all. It sort of feels cleansing. And it'll make you itch like crazy. You'll be really lucky if you hallucinate. Most likely you'll just feel like you've got a fever. Actually, you'll get really hot. And you'll wanna smoke heaps too. I smoke like a train when I'm wasted. What you need to do is get into your pyjamas and sit back and relax. Let it take you over. Put on some music – yeah something trippy. OK, you'll only need this much. See, only a small bubble of air. Let's find that vein. What arm do you use the most? Well your vein will probably be the biggest in that one then. Here hold this around there and keep it tight. Hold the end with that hand. Is it too tight? Tell me if it hurts, OK. Now pump your hand a bit. This might take some time. Where is it? I think it's scared and it doesn't wanna show itself. Just stop for a second. OK, I'll give it a try now. Do you still wanna do it?

Fuck, I've missed! Shit, sorry. Did that hurt? Man, I'm so sorry. I haven't had to do it to someone else for ages. I am really sorry. If I was doing it on myself I could have dug around a little bit to find the vein, but I don't wanna hurt you more than necessary. Just hold your finger there, that'll stop the bruising. Are you all right? You sure? It's OK, we can try the other arm. Here just wrap it a bit higher – yep, that's right – and hold it there. Pump your hand a bit now. Do it a bit faster than that. That's good. Look this one's come up beautifully. Perfect. Much better than the last.

So, do you still wanna do it?

Weeeee!

NATASHA SAMARAS

I was relaxing watching my favourite TV show *Sesame Street* when the TV broke but mummy couldn't fix it. I was upset because I couldn't watch Snuffie, Big Bird or Grover any more, so I went outside to play. I played with my big fluffy dog Digby. He reminds me of Barkley, that orange dog on *Sesame Street*. He is so big and so fluffy he can't see properly because his hair is in front of his eyes. Mummy and Daddy really should give him a haircut so he can see.

I got bored playing with Digby because all he liked doing was playing with the ball, so I went and sat in my yellow swing. My yellow swing is my favourite thing because I love to swing nice and high. I'm not scared to go higher, but my sister Marissa is. My yellow swing is tied to the tree. It's like a box and you sit in it. There are two holes for your legs to stick out. Mummy came out to push me higher. Whee ! Look at how high I can go. One day when I grow bigger, I want to swing really high, so I can touch the sky. I have to eat all my food and drink all my milk to grow bigger. That's what Mummy and Daddy tell me. They are grown-ups and grown-ups know everything.

After a while I didn't want to swing anymore because I needed to go to the toilet. Mummy tried to get me out of the swing, but she wasn't trying very hard, because I was still sitting in it.

'Please Mummy, help me out. I really have to go to the toilet.' Mummy tried and tried to get me out, but I was stuck.

I really wanted to cry, but I didn't because I'm a brave girl and anyway my big cousin John told me that only babies cry, and I wasn't a baby. I told Mummy not to worry, but I think she already was. She ran inside and came out with some soap.

'What's that for, Mummy? It's not bath time now.'

'It's to help make things more slippery. Then you might be able to wiggle yourself out.'

So Mummy made me soapy and slippery. She made lots of little bubbles and I smelt nice, but I still couldn't get out.

'I want Daddy.'

Mummy went inside and rang Daddy. He was at work, so it took a long time for him to come home. I still needed to go to the toilet, and I was really busting, but I didn't say anything. I didn't complain, because I'm a big girl. I tried not to think about it.

Digby was helping me too. He gave me the ball from his mouth and I threw it far away and he brought it back. After that he went to the toilet. All Digby has to do is lift his leg and 'pssssssssshhhhhh', it all comes out. Digby didn't even care that he was doing it all over Mummy's flowers. I don't do that. Watching Digby do his wee reminded me again how much I really had to go to the toilet, so I thought of something else. Food. My favourite food was hot chips and lots of tomato sauce. Mmmmmm, I love when the chips are all soft and mushy, 'cause they feel funny in my mouth.

Ewww, yuck!!!! I'm getting wet. The silly sprinklers have turned on. All that water is making me wet. Water; wee; toilet! Look at all that water spraying everywhere. It's nice and free. Nothing's stopping it from going where ever it wants to go.

'Daddy, you're home. I'm stuck and I can't get out. Can you help me get unstuck?'

'We'll see what we can do.' Daddy went to the shed and brought this big thing with alligator teeth. It looked really scary.

'Daddy what's that thing?'

'It's a saw, sweetie, so I can cut the swing'.

Oh no, not my favourite swing. Now it will be wrecked forever. I hope Daddy makes me another one but next time it will be different. Instead of being like a box, it will be a seat just for big girls. Daddy cut the swing carefully. I didn't even close my eyes. I was very brave. Free at last. I took my pants off and did a wee on the grass, but I didn't mean to do it on the ants too. They were in the way and I couldn't wait any more. Sorry ants. At least I didn't do it on Mummy's flowers.

Autobiography of an Australian

NATASHA SAMARAS

I think God has His reasons for the things He does, and I honestly do believe people when they say 'God works in mysterious ways'. My name is Natasha Samaras, but I was born with a different name. Nineteen years ago, I was born in Seoul, the capital of South Korea. At the time, my Mum was very young, in fact, the same age as I am now. My father never knew about me. When they broke up, he left in search of a new life, in a different place. He was only twenty-one. My Mum did not know she was pregnant, when they went their separate ways. Nine months later I was born In Hee Kim, which means 'to be a kind-hearted and gentle girl'. Unfortunately my Mum could not take care of me, so as soon as I was born, my foster mother took me in. She was being paid to temporarily take care of me by my soon-to-be parents in Adelaide. I was going to be adopted. Since I was only five months old, I do not remember my foster mother, or anything associated with Korea. Maybe that was a good thing. I think if I became too attached, leaving would have been very hard for me.

I arrived in Adelaide at 10:30 am, on 17 September 1979, flight QF 22. My name was changed to Natasha Kim Samaras, which I am grateful for because I think it sounds much nicer than In Hee.

I do not remember ever feeling left out or treated any differently from my sisters. After I arrived, my adoptive parents had three more daughters. Marissa is eighteen, Nicole is fifteen and my little sister Michelle is seven. If anything, I think my family favours me. I do not mean to sound bigheaded, but I know that I have a special place in their hearts. I am not really sure why, but I would like to think it is because I was especially born to be with my family. God had meant it to be this way.

It was much later that I found out why I was adopted. My adoptive Mum fell pregnant to my Dad when she was eighteen. Her parents were very strict, Greek orthodox and believed she had sinned. When they found out, not only were they disgusted in her, she was beaten so badly she could not leave the house. Her face was swollen, covered in bruises and cuts. She had no choice in the matter. An abortion was the only option. Because of this, my Mum and Dad were forced to marry by their parents. When they were ready to start a family, they did not expect it to be so hard. Due to the abortion, carrying a pregnancy to full term was very difficult. After three miscarriages and a lot of heartbreak, my Mum decided to adopt. At first everyone thought she was crazy, but that is what she really wanted. She had already experienced too many losses and adoption was the only way she could find happiness.

People who do not know my family or me are quite surprised to find that I am Greek. I supposed it is not hard to see why they do not believe me. After all, I look very Asian and not at all like a Greek person. The only feature I have in common with my family is my dark hair. Sometimes I laugh when Marissa and I tell a stranger that we are sisters. Most of the times they do not believe us, so we show them our surname and address on our driver's licence.

Other times I am not so amused. I feel embarrassed, awkward, and out of place. Although I have had to explain myself about a hundred times, I still find it difficult to handle.

When I was ten years old, my Grandma made my sisters and me join Greek dancing classes. At the end of the year, we had to perform at a Greek ball in front of many people. I remember feeling very aware of my Asian appearance, amongst all the Greek girls. There I was, dancing in a Greek costume – of course people were pointing and whispering. I could still see them, even though I was dancing.

When I started high school, learning a language was compulsory. I picked Greek, since I had already gone to after-school Greek classes during primary school. From the moment I walked into the class, the students stared at me and whispered to each other. Questions were fired at me, such as 'Why are you doing Greek instead of Chinese?', 'Can you actually speak Greek?' It was situations like these that made me feel uncomfortable.

Every year we go to church at Easter time. I used to dread going, because I was different. It was very uncommon for a non-Greek to go to an Orthodox Church, so everyone was put out by my appearance. In time I have managed to ignore comments that once made me squirm.

Maybe it is because I do not see myself as being Korean, as I have had no experiences with the Korean culture, language or lifestyle. I would be lying if I said that I was just plain Greek. Living in Australia has had a huge influence on who I am today, a Greek-Australian, but mainly Australian. At home we speak English with only a few Greek words thrown into the conversation. I think that now I am older, I do not feel so uncomfortable or out of place. It could be that I am more emotionally mature. Who knows?

Two-and-a-half years ago, my parents separated. This made me very angry because the reason my biological mother gave me up for adoption was so that I could have a loving family, with both parents taking care of me. It took a while for me to realise that I would still have a loving, supportive family, even though my parents could no longer live together.

Some day I hope to meet my biological parents. There are so many things I want to know, things that most people take for granted; for example, who do I look like my Mum or Dad? I would like to know how they are, and if I have any half-brothers or sisters. Although I am now the legal age to find them, I feel I am not quite ready. I can imagine it would be very overwhelming and frightening too.

The only thing I am worried about is offending my adoptive parents. I do not want them to think that I am replacing them, because no one could take their place. My Mum and Dad are the only parents I have known and loved. Hopefully they know how much I love them, so they have nothing to worry about. I am just curious, that is all.

But one day I will find my biological parents, one day soon.

Haiku

A cold misty day –
do not fear the choking blanket
it is only the city fog.

Late in the dark night
I felt a presence close by.
Just my lurking shadow.

Pushing the Precious

Doulton & Co, Wedgwood & Sons, Franklin Mint
– Heirloom Recommended,
Z.S. & Co of Bavaria, Twyford's Vitreous China,
they're all here
– in Limited Edition.
Precious on pedestals. Precious in glass cases.
– On display for all to enjoy.

I have found the true beauty of these precious things
– in wooded galleries.
Where sound echoes with each step
– each breath can be heard by the deafest ear and
Amphoras, containers, carafes and crocks,
Flagons, jars, jugs and pots,
pitchers, urns, vases and vessels,
– silently rest.

In my mind I hear the chaos. The still air broken
By the thorn bird's song. It tempts me, it taunts me.
I creep closer to an old jade owl.
Fingers trembling, I anticipate the crash, the ringing
  smash.
In that triumphant sound, I hear reverberating
One hundred years of kid-gloved care.

Haiku

Morning bungie jump,
Falling from dreams to my bed.
Why is it so hard?

  Blood spills from my jaw,
  These wounds caused by vanity.
  Damn these razor blades.

Ray

Tonight, disturbing scenes as we get up close and personal with those True Blue legends the Battlers. Aussie Mums and Dads protecting ordinary kiddies from the irony of country roads, the emotion of burst water mains, the human face of paedophilia, the dangers of road rage, street offences, street violence, street crime and street kids because parents can't control what the majority of callers think.

We'll show you exclusive eyewitness accounts by innocent bystanders of emotive scenes that some viewers may find disturbing, as we reveal the bizarre true story behind hardened criminals allegedly refusing to comment.

Police *help* rape victim, as we remember the eve of last year's massacre. While the drama unfolds we'll cross LIVE to our reporter
LIVE from the 'STREET OF HORRORS'.

Toby the Pitbull drags my little mate Timmy to safety as Music Industry Personalities in a world's first collaboration raise money for Australia's bravest little hero as tonight he undergoes a heart lung transplant which is all thanks to your support of the dead royal fund.

Haiku

This refreshing verse
CONTAINS PHENYLALANINE
For *LOW JOULE* readers

The Rabbit's Grave

PETER GILES

I'm sitting in my Uncle's backyard. From under his lemon tree the years of rust on the galvanised fence look like they should be my memories. But they're real. There's a small shed in the back corner of the yard. 'Shed' isn't really what you'd call it. It's more of a hutch for the lawn mower and a couple of hammers. My Uncle used to own his own hardware store but he never got round to maintaining a shed; I mean a proper one, you know, one that you could stand in. He always had contractors do the house maintenance. He gave them discounts on tools and equipment and they mended his gutters and mowed his lawns. When he left the business he took a Victa mower, because 'the damn things never break' (a real problem in retail when you're trying to sell to regular customers), two hammers, a shovel, a broom and both kinds of screwdrivers. He said that they should last him through his retirement. The handle on the Phillips head screwdriver cracked a few years later and it had to be replaced, but besides that, he was right. I think the grass needs cutting.

I empty the catcher into the bin and wheel the mower back into its hutch. I notice I have little bits of grass clippings stuck to my trouser legs and brush them away before I sit underneath the lemon tree again.

Aunt Dolly died not long after my Uncle retired. She developed lung cancer, which moved to her liver. Drinking that cocktail of sleeping pills and painkillers was … well it was the right thing for her to do; I think so, anyway. She never complained about the pain but I could see it in her eyes.

My Uncle said he wasn't lonely. He had wonderful memories and visits from me. He also had a pet rabbit named Candice. They would watch TV in a big reclining chair and eat carrots together from a tray fashioned from an old cutting board and Aunt Dolly's ashtray stand. After Aunt Dolly's death my Uncle only seemed happy when Candice was with him.

I pick a lemon from the tree and bite into it. These lemons just haven't been the same since my Uncle stopped pissing on the tree at midnight under the full moon. He said that's all you have to do to have good lemons. I believe him now. My Uncle was always giving me little gems of wisdom like that.

There's the hole in the fence where Candice got out. My Uncle never fixed it. 'No point,' he'd say. 'Too late now.' A sorrowful grimace would cross his face before he'd turn and go inside. He thought that if he had had a handsaw and some wood he might have patched the hole before Candice escaped the safety of the yard. He wouldn't have had to wait for Mr Timms to get round to it the following week.

We buried Candice in the shade of this lemon tree the day we found her. He had few words to say about it. My Uncle missed Candice.

My Uncle died last week. I buried him today next to Aunt Dolly. I'll miss my Uncle.

Haiku

She asked me the time.
I said, 'I don't wear a watch.'
Time was made for slaves.

My wife; gone to work.
She works as a child carer
Who'll make my pancakes?

An Ode to Odes No. 57

There are words for free falling
backwards arms clasped behind your neck
rushing over the edge with your eyes in mine.

There are words for the contents
of the bowl I clasp between my knees when
I am howling sick with disappointment.

There are words, ever words, to
speak in the dark where they slice neatly in
silence unimpeded by light.

There are no words for the compulsion
to apprehend, capture, entwine, obsess, gorge
myself on words that affirm my existence.

Ode to Escapism No. 58

Windows compel me to escape interiors,
the walls that contain
lunchboxes (sticky) schoolbags (disembowelled)
assignments (incomplete) dishes (unclean)
thoughts (impure) beds (too big without you)
child (unwashed) dinner (unmade).

On the other side of that transparent divide
all appears to be as it should. I couldn't improve on that
tree (gracious) fence (farmlike) bougainvillea (ecstatic)
postbox (expectant) sunshine (cliché: cheerful) .

I climb out the window and lose a lifetime in the garden .

Passionfishing

They say goldfish have no memory.

It is true, they rise to the surface at the

promise of food, every time.

In the pool of your bed, deepest green
   sheets, I would rise to your kiss. It is true,
      they touched my libido, every time.

          How I used to strain for a breath of you.
          It is true, you made me arc and
            surface, then you'd turn away, every time.

          Delight for you was watching me writhe
          my golden body across the green. It is true,
          a hungry woman will thrash with splendour.

        My head swimming as you would turn
        your cold shoulder, feigning sleep. It is true,
      I have grown cold lately, cold as a fish.

Nowadays I ignore the movement above me,
sinking deeper into the green. It is true
that a woman has a good memory.
Good as gold.

        Haiku

        Sudden winter, brings
        car park puddles to
        reflect your cold grey eyes.

So I Go No More A-Rowing

The leaky emotional boat that I row
has this one bloody paddle and
I have only a child with little spaghetti
arms to help me row. It's too heavy,

so I go in circles.

> The bed that I toss within never
> traps the dreams it brews
> transient, confused, no intention
> to be realised. It's too empty,

so I rationalise in parables.

The world that I walk through
is densely populated by couples;
grasping, cheating, no role models
to help me believe. It's too unlikely,

so I lament hopelessly.

> The memories that I possess force
> me to live in the past rich with
> scents, touches, tastes and sights to
> help me recall sensuality. It's too distant,

so I hunger incredibly.

The path I choose keeps me
uninspired, famished, questioning too much
Still a child crying for fairness
I shake my head and it won't clear,

so I write poetry .

Bored Games for Adults

DANIELL SIBYLLA

Polaroids are the currency of the game. Like a password, like rolling a six with the dice, you begin the game of philanderous love with a photo of an erection and a scribbled message.

As the game progresses and you move around the bored, you collect other mementos – letters, photos, memories – and piece the rest of the man together. Of course it doesn't matter that he took the photo for your friend: she can't have him either. She played for a while and threw in her hand.

You are at the gateway of 'the other woman land'. You are next in line. He has singled you out next and 'we' don't mind sharing men amongst us. There aren't that many to go around. You make a mental note not to be surprised when you take it in your grip. The polaroid is a secret. The affair is not.

Conveniently, there are only two teams in this game. The 'us' and 'them'. And there is never any doubt who belongs where. For ease of explanation you and I can become US and the married couples become THEM. Let the game begin.

It is a game of sex , desire and love. Not many games combine them all so peculiarly. The husbands (THEM) desire the sex but never cease to love. A foot in each bed, so to speak.

The husbands come with a little deck of cue cards with convenient catch phrases (particularly handy under duress) that read RESPONSIBILITY, FAMILY or COMMITMENT. On the flip side of these there are convenient quips and anecdotal cautionary tales. These cards may be reached for at a speech-less moment when words fail or the husband is cornered into any move that may risk him moving too far from the section of the board that is safe for THEM. The wives may or may not love, but they have no desire. Just the desire to POSSESS. They move about on the board relatively rarely but command an enormous power over the game. They carry a small pack of cards inscribed with their emotional weapons of CHILDREN, GUILT, FINANCE, SEXUAL REWARDS and, likewise, PUNISH-MENT.

The middle section of the board is an intense mix of desire and sex. The wife never moves to that area despite her ability to do so and the beckoning of the husband. This is the risky, heady land that the husband tries to remain in for as long as possible.

The US players are perceived as a perverse, depraved bunch. We are somewhat disadvantaged in that we have to think on our feet. This is not a place for the unimaginative, honest or gullible. The US players have total freedom of movement. Only restricted by the number of children cards you carry. The only way we can be free to pursue one of THEM unrestricted by children is if we have some of their money for baby-sitting or child-care. But remember it is the wife who holds the finances card: ALWAYS. And just try to get a dollar out of a married man. He will bring out his COMMIT-MENT card and reel off a convenient spiel about how he no can do.

And you may wonder how the game ends. We the un-attached, deviant, non-possessed have the ultimate weapon of BLACKMAIL. This unfortunately destroys the world of THEM *and* US immediately. The intrigue dies, the danger, the memories are no longer generated. This is a highly foolish option that no woman chooses more than once. You will be least affected by the blast, but your world dies somewhat none the less. Usually by sheer weight of their security cards and an enormous safety zone, THEY always win. They have a lot to hide behind. Society has constructs that support their righteousness; they have often lived at the same address for years and are prepared usually to stay together in the merest rubble of what they once had. THEY are less corroded by bitterness, less furious, way less compulsive. WE, the erratic fringe dwellers, usually end the game through a kind of emotional malnutrition. Never, ever having a decent meal on our tables. We press our noses to their windows as they glide through their stagnant atmosphere seemingly content to go without those needs we demand as essential.

So the US players have the option to choose the BLACK-MAIL card and annihilate the game – at the same time losing ourselves – or to simply hand the polaroid we took up back to the centre of the board. We also have the option to pass it on to another single friend. She can't believe her luck. He is gorgeous, and she takes up the dice and roll a six. The husbands may commence a new game at any time or conduct several at once. The wives increasingly turn a blind eye and clutch their SECURITY cards.

As for US, we may step off any edge of the board and fall as far as we like. Secure in the paradoxical knowledge that we are utterly desirable and totally unwanted.

This game is also available in the full-colour 'Fable' version which depicts the journey to the castle of the wed ones as a journey up a beanstalk. The goose lays eggs only for the wife, and surprisingly the angry giant is not the wife but the husband who turns on you if you cross his threshold. (Rather a surprising turnaround considering how happily he enters your threshold.) Instead of the polaroid, the game commences with a magic bean that is passed from mistress to mistress.

Beans or polaroids, though, the game is always the same.

Haiku

Exalt the chill of Friday's
pub scenes into torn poetry,
pages of wintry filthy love.

Hare and Tortoise Reunion

MARK TRENWITH

Hey! Hey, tile-back! Yeah you, over near the lamp post! Remember me? Yeah, you know who I am! Hey! Where do ya think *you're* goin? Run all ya want speedy legs, run like the wind. Ha, ha. Go on, I want to see you RUN! Just as I thought! Not so fast now, are ya? I wonder why? Well *I'll* tell ya why tile-back, because you were never fast in the first place! You want to see fast? Here, I'll show you fast! *Whooosh! Whooosh!* Ha, ha, *that's* fast! And so is this, *whooosh* and this, *whooosh*. But of course you wouldn't know anything about runnin' fast, would ya tile-back?

Hey! Hey, come out of there! Ya think if ya hide in that tin can of yours I'll just go away? Well enough hidin' tile-back, we got a score to settle! Hey! Can you hear me in there, you conceited little arse-hole? I said, WE GOT A SCORE TO SETTLE! COME OUT!

Come out of there! Look, if I put ya down, will ya come out? Come on! All right, I'll stop shakin ya, I promise. See I've stopped! I've calmed down now. I won't hurt ya, I promise. *Come on* tortoise, I just want to talk to ya. Ya know. Relive old memories. Come on, I'm not like that any more. You can trust me.

They let me outta the hospital now. They say I'm better, you know. I've come to terms with a lotta things. I just wanna talk for a coupla minutes, then if ya want I'll leave. I promise! Just poke your little head out so I can see ya. Look, I'll stand over here. I'm too far away to even touch ya. Come on.

That's it! Good. See, I just wanna talk. Why? Well, you know ... I thought we could ... you know, catch up. It's been a long time. Yeah, yeah, I know last time we caught up I tried to break ya shell with a pick axe, but I said I was sorry, didn't I? Yeah, yeah, I know I agreed never to come near you again, but I ... Yeah, yeah, I know you have a restraining order, but I'm better now. *Truly* I am. They let me out yesterday. They said I've improved in leaps and bounds. Ha, ha, 'leaps and bounds'! I'm even cracking jokes now! See!

Here, have a carrot. Go on, take one. Oh *go on*! For old times' sake. Whadda ya mean, you're trying to cut down? What are ya? I'm *not* raising my voice! I'm NOT! All I'm tryin'a do is give ya a carrot. That's all. I've been savin' 'em for a while, you know, for somethin' special. There's nothin' wrong with them – they're not drugged or anything, not like that drink ya gave me the night before the race. Oh, it was so! No, I'm not tryin' to start a fight, tortoise, I'm not. I'm not tryin' to make a scene. See, I'm calm! I'm relaxed. I ... I just want ya to admit that ya slipped somethin' in my drink that night.

Look, it doesn't bother me that you did. I don't care, I've come to terms with it now, I just wanna hear ya *say* it an' I'll leave. I want to hear it come outta *your* mouth. Go on, tell me you cheated. Hey! No, stop it! Be quiet! Don't start that up! Just tell me the truth. Come on, did ya or didn't ya drug me before the race? DID YA OR DIDN'T YA? Come on, tell me the truth and then I'll leave! Yeah, I *heard* what you said, but I'm asking for the troooth. No! I, want the ... Oh yeah? YEAH? If that's the truth, then why the hell did I keep fallin' asleep then, huh? HUH! Ya think I was just takin' a happy nap for the hell of it? Well, that's what ya made everyone believe, didn't ya? YEAH! And when all the other animals saw that ya beat me, they wanted to see if ya could beat them as well, didn't they! Yeah, the cheetah, the panther, the ostrich – all the big guns! They all wanted to challenge you too, didn't they? But ya wouldn't have a bar of that, would ya? Nah! You wouldn't race *them*! Not even the *ant*! Why? Were ya too proud to surrender ya crown? Would it mean ya'd lose all your fame? No! They weren't the real reasons! You wanna know the real reason, you manipulating little bastard? You knew you'd only win if they all fell asleep! Isn't that right? And it would all look a bit too convenient if every animal you raced fell asleep, wouldn't it? Yeah! Your plan would've been foiled! YEAH!

Oh that's it! Get back inside your shell! Hide from the truth! Oh, it's the truth all right! An' don't ya go callin' me crazy either ya snide, double-crossing glory-grabber! You're the one who goes slippin' drugs into other people's drinks! Okay, sure, sure, I did lie down for a while – *it was a nice day*! But I wanna know why I was still sleepin' two days after the race, only to wake up with you on the front page of the papers! Yeah, that's what ya' wanted wasn't it? Publicity! Yeah, that's it! First the glamour magazines, then Oprah, then those movie offers! Yeah that was all in ya head even before ya challenged me to that race! Wasn't it!

No-one heard my side of the story, did they? No one apart from a coupla psychiatrists over the years! Yeah, at least *they* listened to me, but everyone just couldn't stop listening to *you*, could they? No! No-one could get enough of *tortoise*. Well, it's too bad ya didn't tell em about how ya' cheated, isn't it! Well I say it's about time ya did! Go on, tell the world! Tell the world ya cheated, you little son-of-a-bitch! You robbed me, you arse-hole! I should've been Father of the Year, I shoulda been number one on *Who Weekly*'s Famous Faces list, I shoulda been photographed having lunch with Diana Ross! It shoulda been me! You cheated, you little son of a bitch! YOU CHEATED! YOU CHEAT!

Hey, hang on! I … Just excuse me for a sec … I think … HEY! Hey, you there! Yeah, you over near the bin! Yeah, I thought it was you! Remember me, snail? Remember ME?

ANNEMARIE GOODWIN

Rush

Tipped off the boat deck
Without my floaties
Prematurely dumped
Into the blue rush.

Headfirst, arms flailing
Shell nails breaking
Through the blue window
Onto the sea floor.

Watery chatter
Besieged my eardrums
Cerulean palms
Stroked my bones awake.

Sweeping through space
Electric starfish
Exposed every nook
In this kelp kingdom.

Arrowing through the halls
Of jade and silver
Shimmering swordfish
Soon overtook me.

Brushing past algae
Your coral fingers
Cradled me inside
Aquatic gardens.

My earth chains loosened
I found my fish flesh
Felt the mermaids' hearts
Hammering the depths.

Forgetting our feet
We twined like seaweed
Squeezed apart the sand
Anchoring our skin.

Marine foliage swayed
To the gentle ebb
And sigh of the tides
Echoing above.

Parting the surface
Equipped with life jackets
Skindivers arrived
To sever the weed.

Haiku

A single fire-fly
Encircled by the globed sky;
Light bulb filament.

Understanding Men

ANNEMARIE GOODWIN

'Eyes! Expression! Face! Not like that. More *tragic!*'

'Like this?' I add to the list of things to remember – shoulders down, elbows lifted, back long, stomach in, feet stretched, supporting leg held tight – the phrase *Be More Tragic.*

'Not quite.' Ms Reed jabs at the pause button on the tape recorder. 'Of all the major ballets, *Giselle* is the most tragic. Don't look happy. Think trauma! Then put it into your dancing.'

'Yes, Ms Reed.' I complete my final *arabesque en fondu* in what I imagine to be a wistful manner.

'Not enough!' She punches the pause button a third time. 'I'll be looking for the appropriate expression, and if it's not there I'll be replacing you with your understudy. Understand?'

'Yes, Ms Reed.'

'I'd *rather* see you give me the expression I'm after … Understand?'

'Yes, Ms Reed.'

'The director of America's biggest classical ballet company will be in the audience Saturday night. You know what that means. Remember all the strings I had to pull to get him here? I've told him that you're *the* Australian dancer worth recruiting. Prove me right. *Please.*' She motions the corps to come back onstage.

'Yes, Ms Reed.'

I limp towards the nearest wing. Undoing the ribbons on my pointe shoes, I wonder how I'm going to convey a sense of tragedy I've never felt. Actually, Giselle is a damned hard person to relate to: a naive peasant who mistakes mere flirtation on Prince Albrecht's part for love, and goes mad with grief once she finds out his true feelings. I feel the antithesis of her. I always view promises of fidelity from males under the age of 35 with scepticism. I've erased the words 'love' and 'relationship' from my vocabulary. Giselle's expectation that flirtation would be followed up with a marriage proposal seems idealistic; her belief in her ability to sustain a male's attention naive.

The walk down the blue-carpeted corridor to the dressing room takes forever. My leg muscles are on fire. My leotard is swimming in sweat. Only my feet are cool. Released from the pointe shoes, my toes continue to ache. The sound of Ms Reed's voice penetrates the wall separating the corridor from the stage. Nadia, it seems, is now the target of Ms Reed's vocal bombardment.

Not that we would want things any other way. Our friends are no doubt still sitting, gossiping, in the back of a classroom somewhere. I'm glad I'm not there with them.

By the same token, it's been a long time since I've run amok. Travelling from the hotel to the theatre each day, I see yobbos on street corners giggling at nothing. I overhear preteens agonising over what colour they should paint their nails. I envy their total lack of responsibility.

Unfastening my hairnet, I glance up at the clock. I'm finding it hard to comprehend that I don't have to be anywhere doing anything tonight. Ms Reed leaves the night before a performance free so we can rest. To us, the word 'rest' means anything from making a quiet phone call home before falling asleep, to enjoying a night on the town. I fall into the latter category. I'm looking forward to a night on the town. Nadia has left her side of this pint-sized box called a dressing 'room' immaculately tidy. Good. We should be able to pack up and get back to the hotel before nightfall.

Passing from the chill of the July evening into the warmth of the club, I feel as though opening night is a zillion hours away. Nadia and I pace the floor, searching for familiar faces. We see none. Reaching the dance floor, we meld with the intoxicated crowd.

The Star Lounge complex is much larger than it appears from outside. The mirrored walls and ceiling of this nocturnal gymnasium create multiple images. Hip-hop rhythms bounce from capacious speakers. A flashing neon illuminates a spiral staircase. Velvet steps lead to every clubgoer's idea of heaven: the bar. Placing a cautious hand on the silver rail, I glance back at the pulsing crowd. Catching my eye, Nadia nods to indicate that she's seen where I'm heading. She holds up a finger, indicating that she wants just the one drink. Sub Zero is her favourite – I think.

The ceiling and walls of the upper level consist entirely of glass. Reflections off a mirror ball minnow along the glassy expanse. Out of this colossal fish bowl faces emerge. Groups of people wander the crowded balconies, sucking delicately on cigarettes. Through air tightly laced with spools of smoke their incandescent faces flash like falling stars. A fluorescent strobe begins to stalk my shoulders and neck. Drenched in light, I float towards the immense bar.

Halfway across the floor I am caught by the glitter of a stranger's eyes. He resembles a model recently featured in some upmarket advertising campaign; his face flawless, his hair gelled to perfection ... The vision is too much: I slip through the nearest doorway away from his sight.

Leaning up against the balcony rail, I feel the cool palms of night stroke my forehead and arms. The stars overhead glint like cats' eyes. Car headlights teem in the black expanse beneath the street lights.

The words *Purple Palace Pool Hall* sprawl the length of the wall opposite. A heavy techno beat emanates from the building. Shadowy figures move behind the french windows which provide access to the balcony. The outlines of bent backs and beer bellies appear grotesquely large. Slivers of raucous conversation reach my ears. I could stand here forever, watching the car lights swarm around the static orange lights. Instead, shivering, I turn back to the warmth of the club.

He is still there. Not doing anything in particular. Just watching. And dancing. A little. Close up, he looks impossibly perfect. My expression warns him away. I hope. I'm not the type to use a person once. I'm not that superficial. Nor that desperate. Nevertheless, when his hands start to slide around my skin, I don't push them away.

All too soon we are outside, hurrying though the icy streets towards the car. The city lights shine all around us: sober shades of orange and white.

The purr of his electric heater wakes me. Rolling onto my side, I watch the bed linen flutter in response to the rush of hot air. A gap in the curtains reveals the time of morning; traces of mist still simmer through cauldron-black hills. The dawn somersaults slowly over the champagne carpet in tangled rays, eventually settling on his face.

I watch him as he sleeps, touching his face with my fingertips. I watch him as he dreams, seeing his forehead tense, then calm. I watch him as he wakes, feeling one drowsy hand stir then reach involuntarily for mine.

'Sugar?' I push a packet towards him.

'Ta.' As he reaches for it our fingers brush; he takes hold of my hand.

'You know …' I quickly gulp down my latte.

'What?' His smile is innocent, affectionate.

'You know …' I wriggle in my seat. Then clear my throat. 'I can't see you anymore.'

'I understand.' My face blanches.

'I liked being with you. But it's better we end it now. It's too hard for us to have a relationship.'

'But …'

'I don't want a relationship with anyone right now. In the

future, maybe. Not now.'

'I understand.'

'It's best if we just forget it. Okay?'

'But ...'

'Last night was just ... I didn't *feel* anything. There was no attraction.'

'I understand.'

'Look, you didn't mean anything. It was just a physical thing.'

'But ...'

'I was also plastered. I don't remember much.'

'I understand.'

'Okay. I'll admit you looked ... you stood out. You seemed ... innocent.'

'I ...' His lips move then stop.

'But you're not.'

Of course I want to see him again. He doesn't want to see me. I can tell. So I get in first. Say the very words he intended to say.

He looks relieved. I have been successfully disposed of. He is restless. Bored. Ready for the next night, the next experience.

We sit motionless, two urban statues surrounded by bright, white tables, plastic chairs and tawdry alfresco umbrellas. We listen to the cosy titter of the group sitting at the next table. The babble associated with the breakfast rush dies. We stand. I walk away quickly. Back to the hotel. Back to the performance.

Back to playing *Giselle*.

Be Seeing You

JEREMY GILL

The band inside the cafe was relentless in its percussion. The windows rattled and the crowd inside moved in an orgasmic frenzy. At his table, he could feel the beat coming through the wall. He closed his eyes behind his dark sunglasses and let himself dissolve into the bass. His two friends at the table were laughing at their own jokes and pointing out attractive women to each other. He tuned them out.

The band finished the set. His friends decided to go to the bar, to hunt. He felt the fear returning. He felt alone in the silence. Taking deep breaths, he relaxed. His senses stretched out to find a distraction, a focus. Nothing, nothing, wait … that voice. He raised his head and concentrated on the voice. Oh God, he thought, it's her.

She had sat down and ordered. She was angry. Her mind screamed out her indignation at the humiliation that she'd suffered. Those remarks, the laughter. She swore at them. The two swine backed off. She felt sick. She had tried to ignore them by talking on her cellular phone to her five-year-old daughter but eventually she looked back at the table of wolves.

She has a daughter … *We* have a daughter … *I* have a daughter, he thought. He strained to listen for a name, anything. He knew her age. He remembered her conception.

The smell of beer, the warmth of two beneath the blanket. Fumbling, confusion, and fear – always fear.

Humiliation, running, running, falling, carlights, broken glass, twisted metal, twisted body. Pain. Darkness. Alone in the silence.

She stared at the table. It was him. Oh God …

The excitement, feeling wanted, special. The romance, the intimacy, the kiss. Snuggling in a bed, the heat, the moment … and he was gone. The loneliness, the pain. Anger.

He looked pale and had lost a lot of weight. She felt secure that she looked better after five years than he did.

'Hello,' she said.

'Hello.'

'I see you recognise me.'

Silence. Then:

'Yes,' he murmured

One word, one tone. Hate?

'You left me.'

'I know … I'm sorry.' Apology in his voice.

She wished that she could see his eyes.

'I went away,' he continued

'*I'm sorry,*' she mimicked, '*I went away.* What about me?' she suddenly screamed.

He raised his head and she saw the first glimmer of emotion on his face. Confusion?

'You left me alone, you bastard, and … nothing. Where were you? What did I do?'

Silence, his head in his hands.

'We have a child,' she sobbed.

No response.

'You knew, didn't you? There was no surprise just now when I told you. You *bastard.*'

'Wait.' His whisper silenced her and he took off his glasses.

'Omigod! I'm sorry,' she stuttered. 'I didn't know.'

He didn't mimic her.

He gave her his address and she left, promising to visit

with their daughter. He could tell she would, by her voice. He was good at voices. When his mates returned he told them that he'd find his own way home. Reluctantly, they agreed.

He finished a coffee, unfolded his white cane.

'Be seeing you,' he said as he left.

Cigarette Breakfast

The Sleeper awakes, the dunny – two shakes
A ciggy and coffee in hand
Then I am King and the world is at spring
As I survey the land.

The warmth without that comes within
Strikes me to the core
But to ensure that my spirit is pure
I smoke and drink some more.

The nicotine kickstarts my lungs
The caffeine speeds up my heart
If I went to the beach and gave a speech
Surely the seas would part.

Then the calm washes over me
And sanity makes me sick
Not touched by God, I'm only odd –
A fool with a cancer stick!

Mourning Break

JEREMY GILL

It's 1.30 in the afternoon and all the residents have been toileted. As the Activities Planner of the nursing home, it's my job to ensure that the residents are occupied in activities that hopefully, in some way, are beneficial to their well-being and are age-appropriate. It's difficult. I put on a video – Gene Kelly, I think; I like Gene Kelly – and it's a quiet afternoon so I decide to check out the rest of the nursing home, to see if any of the bedfast 'ressies' need a channel swapped or their bedding changed or a chat.

I walk out of the living room to the hallway, where I can see right down to the front door. Four wards branch off the corridor. I look at the polished floor, shining in its cleanliness and contrasting with the revolting lime colour of the walls. The prints on the wall show no consistency of style or taste. The decor of ugly vases with plastic flowers is an unconvincing attempt to mask the reality of decay and sadness, which manifests itself in the smell of disinfectant.

I pop my head into the first room on my left; everything okay, Mrs Wallace knitting and Miss Edan muttering in her sleep. A couple of steps and I look into the room on the right; Allie is upright in bed, eyes shut.

No, this is wrong.

I walk up to her, on the right side of the bed, studying her face. I look away, at the cleaner who frowns at me. I think, can't she see anything wrong? The cleaner knows that I think something is wrong, but I know that I have no expression. I look back at Allie, dismissing the cleaner. She can't help me in this, she is a cleaner.

Allie's face is grey and yellow, and her tongue is protruding, covered in saliva, bubbling. There is no movement – in her face, in her arms, in her chest. I touch her cheek, hopeful that she will flinch or move her face away from the foreign presence which disturbs her rest.

Nothing. I quickly check the carotid pulse. Again nothing.

I gently move some stray hairs from her forehead and caress her cheek. 'Oh Allie,' I sigh.

At the sound of movement, I look at the cleaner.

'Is she … ?' she whispers.

I nod. I return to the hall and see the sister.

'You'd better check on Allie,' I say. She frowns, but changes when she sees the expression on my face. What expression, I wonder.

The sister meets me at the sink in the nurses' office and starts to wash her hands, so I move over.

'I think you're right,' she says.

With an expressionless voice I ask if I can go out for a cigarette. Again she studies my face and finally nods as I take my expressionless mask outside. I finish my cigarette and go back in, ready to strip the bed and remake it for the new resident who will be coming that afternoon. We never run out of old people.

Mourning break is over.

Freedom from the Body

NICOLE DICKMANN

S he turned the tap ever so slightly to the right. Cool water came gushing out of the shiny metal shower head. She placed her hand underneath the flowing stream and tested its warmth. Her hand flinched at the touch of the cold water, and retreated back to the natural warmth of the air.

She adjusted the taps until the water flow became an inviting heat that made her slender body step into its reach. The colourless flow touched her body and cleansed her pores of filth. As each water droplet touched her body it seemed to communicate, and in response her mind and body were set free.

She moved her feet forward to stand in the pool of water that had formed on the cold shower floor. She felt a burning sensation in her toes as her feet attempted to adjust to the temperature. Her feet began to warm as they simultaneously relaxed.

The water surged from the shower head and onto her tender skin. The force was so soft, yet she knew its power. She turned her back towards the stream, to let her muscular back feel the cleansing sensation. She arched like a cat, to feel every single droplet greet and then deflect off her, like a shield.

Her head met the flow of water and soon her long hair was saturated. Her once soft and gentle hair tightened around her neck, and water began to run down her chest. Each drop followed a path which had its own purifying effect. Drops of water rounded at the ends of her hair, and then dropped, almost hesitantly, onto her delicate breasts. Others fell onto her back and then slid down, on the surface of her body, following the gentle curves.

Her mind was freed from everything that had once taken control of her time. Work, her family, her boyfriend and her best friend, Julie, all escaped her thoughts without reluctance. Her mind filled with warm and tender thoughts, like a wave in the sea taking its own unpredictable path that no-one could follow.

She stared at the white ceiling as if it were the one thing that enabled her to hold onto this precious moment. She lifted her hands and placed them on the Roman-tiled wall in front of her. The cold, yet welcoming support kept her standing as she felt a wave of nausea sweep through her entire body. She closed her eyes and tried to regain her thoughts.

Her boyfriend's face appeared in her mind and she could smell his aroma and after-shave. She remembered when he had tried to scare her one day last week, in the shower. He had entered the white, sparkling bathroom without her knowing, and when she turned, she had screamed and fallen over.

He had tried to help her up but the mixture of soap, shower gel and water made the tiles slippery and he fell down too. They laughed uncontrollably, to their dismay, realising that they were now closer than they had been for some time. Whether from lack of time, or perhaps effort, the humorous moment turned into a sensual one of passion and excitement.

She had lost it. She had lost the peace and frame of mind that she often showered for. The one time when she could be without care or thought ... the time she longed for, without pressures. She could release herself and feel as if she were floating somewhere, above all her problems.

Now her mind was full of her pain and anguish. The thought of her mother and father both dying slowly of lung cancer was enough to make her weep; the thought of her best friend sleeping with her long-time boyfriend just made it worse.

She stretched her head back so that the water ran down

her tired face. The water hit her eye sockets and began to force out the tears. She placed her hands over her eyes and tried to stop the pain. In anger, she slid her hands down her face with great force, revealing her bloodshot, weary eyes. She let out a loud piercing scream that echoed on the walls and seemed to carry on for hours inside her heart.

Her knees buckled and she found herself lying painfully on the shower floor. The water splashed all around her body, almost teasing her now. She placed her hands on the cold, merciless ground and tried to force herself up. Her lack of strength prevented her from standing and leaving the now grim shower. She extended her legs so that they touched the other side of the shower wall and then she pushed violently, attempting to escape her suffering.

She lent forward gradually, until her eyes met the shower drain. The water drops from the shower head were now gone and trackless. The drain had formed a small whirlpool around itself, and water from everywhere was rushing to enter its kingdom. She wished that she could follow the water, down the drain, perhaps into a new world of love and freedom, with no pain, deceit or agony.

Just as she was about to scream again, the bathroom door opened. A lady in a white dress walked in abruptly and opened the shower door. She reached into the shower, turned off the taps, and said, 'Hurry up will you, Carrie, you've been in here long enough.'

Carrie was confused. She looked up at the lady, then back down to the shower floor. She wasn't sure whether to laugh, scream or cry. The lady placed her hand underneath Carrie's arm and yanked her up with a strength that left her arm aching.

Carrie looked down at her body with embarrassment, then attempted to cover her breasts. The lady just laughed and threw an old shaggy brown towel at her. The towel didn't offer much protection, but she knew it would have to do. She wrapped the rag around her naked body. The lady pulled

Carrie out of the shower and attempted to push her out of the bathroom.

Carrie would have left the bathroom willingly but she noticed that something was different. A new light was shining on the comfortable, inviting bathroom and it suddenly became unpleasant and disturbing. She lifted her head and looked around the Roman-tiled bathroom, only to see that the walls were colder than one could imagine and that they made her feel lonelier than ever. The grey walls were concrete, with cracks running from every corner, and there were no Roman tiles to be seen.

Carrie's mouth dropped as her eyes wandered around the strange room. She looked at the shower that she had been washing in so few minutes ago and saw a rusted, metal shower head and a rusted drain. The shower door was nothing but a stingy curtain with more holes than material.

Then she remembered where she was and her mind was filled with painful thoughts. She placed her hands over her ears to try to stop the thoughts entering her mind but nothing could prevent them. The lady forced her hands into Carrie's back and pushed her towards the door once again. This time, Carrie let her body comply with the nurse's demands and she walked sullenly back to the psychiatric ward, where she would await another shower … to free her mind again.

Arrival

SHAUN DAVIS

My boots crunch as I walk slowly along the gravel road and, except for the wind, it is the only sound in the night that I can hear. The wind moans through the surrounding forest, causing the shadowy outlines of the trees standing over me to bend. I feel as if they are reaching for me, trying to pick me up in their decaying limbs to crack my bones. Above them, a bloody moon shines down; its dull light reflects onto the dew on the grass creating a red-silver blanket that runs towards the tree-line. Ahead, the path continues up a small incline and I can see the light of the city I am heading towards mingling with the navy blue sky.

Upon reaching the top of the hill, I am assaulted by a blast of chill air which has rushed off the ocean, to greet me like an old friend. It hits me full in the face, whipping back my hair and tearing through my clothes. I pull my fur-lined velvet cloak tighter around me in an attempt to protect myself; however I might as well be wearing a simple night-shirt for all the good it does. For twenty years now such winds have caused my mind to jump back to this place; now I have come back to face my past and those icy memories.

Recovering some poise, I soak up the sight from the top of the hill. Spread out to the north and south lies the immense city of Tanduin. Next to me the dead, spindly forest has thinned out; dead grass covers the ground for two hundred metres until great slabs of worked black stone rise up from the earth. The fifty-foot walls encompass the entire city and extend into the sea, providing the harbour with both defence and a breakwater. Standing next to the gates that allow ships onto the sea are two black stone lighthouses; a blue-white light pulses hypnotically from the top of each building, illuminating the harbour. I briefly close my eyes, trying to block out their light. In my mind's eye I can remember the crowd: the press of human flesh and those people who fell while running but were crushed before they could regain their footing. I remember hanging onto my mother's neck, looking back over her shoulder as we fled the city; and I remember that pulsing strobe light highlighting the death around me for one moment and then blocking it out the next.

I open my eyes and take a deep breath, steadying myself. I lift my hand to shield my eyes from the eerie light. Looking beyond the city's walls I see blackness; blackness punctuated by the pulse of the lighthouses. The landscape, in those brief moments, is revealed, showing burnt-out buildings and empty streets. Dwarfing those structures are the domes and spires of various churches compacted together next to the market quarter. Magnificent artwork and colourful stained-glass windows are highlighted even in the dark by huge blazing torches of blue fire which adorn the walls and the ground in front of the massive shrines. The half-a-dozen churches make up what was once called The Gods' Circle. Now its name has probably changed, for it is there (I have learned) that the slaves, human breeding stock and the enemies of Tanduin are kept.

Slightly elevated and in the north quarter of the city lies the once majestic Crystal Palace. Standing taller than any other structure in the city and with spires that climb towards the clouds, its scale alone demands one's attention. However, most captivating of all are the palace walls, which seem to be carved out of obsidian. The walls that once seemed to generate their own splendid luminescence now pulse with an emerald-green glow, in perfect timing with the demonic pulse of the lighthouses.

The wind blowing off the sea picks up in strength. I tear my eyes away from the palace that was once my home, forced back into reality by that cutting wind. I gather my cloak around me once again, but no amount of clothing can warm my spirit. I begin walking toward the city, every reluctant step bringing back dark memories.

I close my eyes again as I walk. I can smell smoke, death and raw sewage in the ocean breeze. On the same wind the screams of torment are carried to me, probably from the area that was once the church district. As I get closer the screams grow louder.

The walls now look down on me. I have to tilt my head right back to see the top of the fifty-foot structure. In front of me is a double-reinforced oak gate. It extends two-thirds up the height of the wall. Hanging on the walls are human heads in various states of decay. On some of them I can see dark shapes moving, feasting on the skulls. I get closer to the gate; nailed to it with arms spread is a human form. Thick steel spikes are nailed through each eye socket and with every gust of wind his torn clothing flaps open, revealing a gutted husk. A moan escapes the corpse's lips and I wonder what sort of black art has been used to keep the person alive and aware. Sudden movement draws my attention upwards and I can see someone on top of the wall silhouetted against the nightline.

A voice, the sound of paper tearing, calls out to me ...

(Extract from work in progress)

Haiku

The sapphire blue sky;
White foam explodes over stone –
The strength of the sea.

The storm hides the moon;
The rain pours onto the trees –
Lightning splits a trunk.

Silence

VENITA POBLOCKI

Stark silence. Only my feet crunch the dry, yellow grass. It reflects the sun into my eyes and burns my retinas. I look away sharply to the sky and see nothing but white blotches. I stop a while until I can see clearly again, then continue walking to the clothesline. Blades of grass stick up and I am fearful they will cut the webbing between my toes. Every step I brace myself for the severing. It doesn't happen. My basket of clothes, a burden propped on my hip like a heavy child, begins to slip from my embrace and drops as I reach the line. The bleached, scaly pegs hang limp from the wire – the only pastel in this sickly sweet surrounding.

My thin dress blows between my legs and I am scared my thighs look too fat. I fight the wind and pull it out, only for it to blow back in. I continue hanging up the clothes. In front of me the galvanised iron fence ripples its way around the yard. I am surrounded by heat I cannot escape. It reflects off all sides. It penetrates my body until it is an internal heat I cannot avoid. It makes me anxious and sweat uncomfortably.

I crunch from foot to foot on the lawn, wiping my feet against my calves to get rid of the burrs. My breasts ache and my back is sore. I hang up my bra. I hang on to the wire and drop my head between my dry elbows. I take a deep breath and close my eyes. Inhale. Exhale. I hang. The wire cuts into my fingers. I can hear the neighbour's transistor turn on. Her baby begins to cry – no, it's mine. I transfer my weight to my other leg. My head hangs. Inhale. I turn and leave the line behind me. I walk until I escape the front gate. I close it behind me. Exhale. I walk and walk and walk. Barefoot and pregnant without a kitchen. I walk down the cracked footpath. I hear the transistors, the babies, the sobbing wives. I walk.

A cool breeze begins to blow softly from nowhere. My hair takes flight and curls kick gently in the air. The burning in my eyes is cooled. My feet feel no sticks and stones. I walk and I don't stop. I hear chirps of happy birds. The kookaburra laughs and I can't help giggling. I walk on. The green grass is closer now. Light green now dark green. Clover. My skin is rehydrated, and my internal burning, my yearning is quenched. I feel light and my steps are graceful yet powerful. I don't stop walking. My feet swish confidently through the grass. I leave suburbia. I undo the buttons on my dress. The breeze rushes in and evaporates the sweat between my breasts. My dress blows off, twisting behind me but I keep walking. The stream up ahead is lined with trees and bushes. I can hear it flowing. It's calling.

With each breath I am rejuvenated; I am restored piece by piece. Completeness is mine. I look at myself in the water, removing my underwear. The chattering of the life around holds me. The rounded pebbles clunk as I step in. The water tickles around my calves. I make my way out to the middle. I stop there and stand. Naked. The shade is gentle, inside and out. The water is soothing, inside and out. I stand like Venus. Hair drifting, nothing covered. Then I laugh. I laugh out loud with the birds, plonking myself down in the water. I drink a mouthful and splash the rest on my face. I breathe deeply. The hardened air leaves. Bubbles gush around me. I tilt my head back, my body rises and I float. I hold my pregnant belly and float. I am not scared.

I go *with* the water.

Bubble-Man

Venita Poblocki

'Bubble-Man? Is that you? Bubble-Man? So noble Bubble-Man, in the bottom of your aquarium, your tank.'

Beaty taps on the glass. Tick, tick, tick. Tap, tap, tap. Bubble-Man.

The filter's buzz vibrates between Beaty's ears. Drowning out other noise. Totally absorbed in Bubble-Man. Bubble-Man. Tick, tick, tick. Tap, tap, tap. The Bubble-Man, looking straight into Beaty's eyes, lives in the bottom of the tank bubbling the water for the fish. So friendly and kind of him. He lives a lonely life. Fish can't talk. Alone there, standing small in his fishbowl helmet, flippers and wetsuit. Staring into the outside world, into Beaty's eyes.

'Bubble-Man?'

'Yes?' Bubble-Man replies in his synthetic bubble-voice.

'Bubble-Man … I love you,' declares Beaty.

'I love you, too,' declares Bubble-Man.

Beaty immerses himself in watching the crystal bubbles rise from Bubble-Man's head. An endless stream zooms out and up, up – myriad spheres – perfect beauty. Beaty watches. Eyes wider than wide, one pupil dilating, almost all blue. The other, a mere pinprick. Mouth gaping, hanging flaccid, wide-open, breathing raspy, lips puffy, pink, moist. His warm breath fogging the glass. Beaty wiping it with his sleeve inter-mittently. Swipe and squeak. Swipe and squeak. Right arm, squeak. Colours brighter, clearer than ever before.

F f r r r tttt. The fart bubbles up his crack. 'Not like your bubbles, Bubble-Man.' No smile coming to Beaty's face. Dead serious.

'Bubble-Man?'

'Yes?'

'Bubble-Man? What world do you live in?'

'Your world, Beaty, your world.'

'Hmmm. Good.' A quick gasp. A new idea.

'Bubble-Man? Do you want some chips?' Beaty's right arm extends, eyes still attached to Bubble-Man. Clasps packet, brings to body. Grabs chip, never losing sight of Bubble-Man. Puts chip in mouth. Crunches. 'Yummo. Good. I'll give you one, Mr Bubble-Man.'

Beaty tries to put a chip in the tank. He forgets to remove the lid. The chip crunches. His fist punches through the glass and it shatters. Shards shred his arm. Beaty screams, panics. Bubble-Man is knocked over, loses his breathing tube and the crystal bubbles end. The last two leave his helmet.

'Don't worry Bubble-Man. I'll rescue you. I'll help you. I'll fix you.'

Blood from Beaty's sliced hand swirls in the perfect water. Glass slices his hand further, deeper. Kicking up gravel with his clumsy fingers. For the first time Beaty loses sight and contact with Bubble-Man.

Bubble-Man's electronic voice can be heard. 'Can't breathe, Beaty! Can't breathe!' Beaty's own breath becomes limited and tight. The higher than high-pitched scrapes of gravel on the tank fill his head. Fragments of glass puncture Beaty's veins.

The chips, bloated, bob on the tidal waves of water. Beaty's tattered, red hand clasps Bubble-Man's body from beneath the murk. Withdraws from tank.

'Bubble-Man! Bubble-Man!' Terrified, bloodied. 'Bubble-Man!'

'Breathe! Can't breathe, Beaty.'

Beaty's throat clenches tighter. Left hand grasps throat.

Little breath is drawn. Very little … None. Still clasping Bubble-Man, Beaty turns blue. Sea blue. Sky blue. Blue. Pink lips turn blue. Vision fades. Colours die. Beaty smashes against the tank. Fish, now fuzzy shades of grey, flap on the ground. Flip, flap. Flip, flap. Beaty lays thrashing with them. Then jerking. Soaked in pondweed, water, crushed glass, making bubbles. Bubble-Man in right hand. Grip never ending.

'Bu … bhl … Ma ….'

Blue. Bloodied. Wet. Breathless. Lifeless. Both Bubble-Man and Beaty die.

The stench of Beaty's warm death-shit fills the room. Bubble-Man, as stiff as ceramic, rolls from Beaty's life … or rather, death.

Review

BETHANY JORDAN

The three authors booked for the presentation have all managed to be late, but it doesn't appear to bother the audience. Nor does the stifling heat deter them; in fact its only effect is to emphasise their exuberance. Voices rise, gestures grow wilder and egos clash as the women laugh, chatter and boast. As the lone male in the audience – as well as being a quiet and reserved man – William Bennett ought to look uncomfortable, but he doesn't. He has spent most of his life surrounded by would-be writers: now they simply amuse him. His small smile turns to a chuckle as the two women either side of him suddenly recognise each other and flatten him in their gleeful embrace.

A crocodile of school children enters loudly. There aren't enough seats, so the children scramble to find a bit of grass near the front. William tries to arrange himself to accommodate them, but the seat is too small and his long legs stretch awkwardly in front of him. Unperturbed, two of the children use his legs as leaning posts, after a quick glance upwards for his permission. Nodding his agreement, he resigns himself to an uncomfortable hour.

Next to arrive is a young woman of about twenty. Looking at her, William is reminded of his own daughter, although their only connection is age. While his daughter is tall and blonde, this woman is small, with a mane of curly brown hair. She wears purple pants with pink elephants on them and a bright green t-shirt. Her bright blue bag is also adorned with elephants. She flings it around, hitting various members of the audience as she struggles to find a seat. Laughing apologies, she finally settles herself into the seat directly behind William, and proceeds to empty her bag in search of a pen. Although her loud clothes are completely contrary to William's own sober style he likes them, and he likes her for wearing them. William usually judges people by their clothes, an unfair but often accurate way of understanding people. He turns to run his practised eye over the three authors who have sauntered in at last, murmuring something about a flat battery. William dislikes them immediately, suspecting that their lateness had little to do with car troubles and a lot to do with the wish for a grand entrance. William's sense of humour diminishes when faced with obvious arrogance. Conscious of his own intolerance, he orders himself to reserve judgement until they have at least begun their speeches.

The next half hour only serves to confirm his first impression. Each author uses their ten minutes to list everything they have ever written, all the awards they have won and all the good things said about them. William scowls; these are the people who encourage the stereotype that all writers are completely self-absorbed. He knows that the majority of writers are actually lacking in confidence, but they are not usually the ones present at Writers' Week. He entertains the possibility of leaving, but a glance at the children at his feet and the crowds on either side soon squash that idea.

The next half hour is reserved for questions, but is monopolised by the children with notes carefully prepared in their exercise books. One by one they stretch up to the single microphone and ask 'What sort of books do you like?' and 'Did you always want to be a writer?' The authors respond with clichés in condescending tones and special smiles.

William rebukes himself for attending; he can't bear to watch these people who write pulp fiction and holiday reading talking about their inspiration. Just as he's working himself up into a silent rage the child on his left leg pops up with the inevitable question 'Where do you get your ideas from?' Before the authors can reply a steady, clearly audible voice comes from behind him: 'K-mart'.

The audience is unimpressed. Silence fills the small tent as the authors struggle to continue. William is convulsed with laughter. The spoken words have echoed completely his thoughts in a way he had never dared. He doesn't need to turn around to see who uttered them; they obviously came from a pink-and-purple pants wearer.

Thinking about her, William is filled with a sense of rebellion. Never, in his sixty-six years, has he spoken his mind without thinking about the consequences. Never has he voiced the sarcastic comments which constantly dance around in his head. Admiration sweeps over him as he thinks about this woman who has so little sense of responsibility at so young an age.

Perhaps it is her age, perhaps it is her generation. Well damn his own generation for not allowing him such fun. And damn himself for caring about what other people think. William drags himself back from his thoughts to tune into the speakers in front of him. One author is continuing on the dreary line of where she gets her ideas.

'Sometimes they just take you by surprise; say, when listening to a piece of music. Sometimes they can be ideas that have been hanging around for years, and can be used in a new way.'

Here she pauses. For the first time in his life William seizes the moment.

'Red light sales.'

He doesn't care what the author thinks. He doesn't care about the loud *tsk*s coming from the audience. He only cares about his own sense of fulfilment, and the sound of a young woman's loud giggles behind him.

Home

BETHANY JORDAN

It looks like one of those découpage pictures, everything overlapping. The trees start small closest to me and get bigger as the eyes grow wider. They've always been there. To the left is a green shed. 'Distressed', but really just old.

The cats model in the corner. The dog – there is always a dog – is also asleep but looks less picturesque than the cats. They wake as a waft of wind comes from the neighbour's yard. They're barbecuing again.

It seems as if the sun has studied the view and added a few touches of light to complete the picture. In the middle of all the glory is the washing line. 'Hello. I'm necessary.'

There's a water tank, useless now, but it belongs. Occasionally the *bork, boork* of the chooks floats into the air. They're hidden, but of course they're there. The sky is blue. It seems as if the sky should always be blue, but then it rains, and that's right too.

There's the hose wrapped around the tap on the wall. The flowers scattered, the dropped leaves, the lawn mulch.

So predictable. It's average. It's typical. It's home.

The trees at the back are twice the size of the house. I know; I've climbed them. The strings on the clothesline are still low, originally positioned to be accessible to little arms. They were made too low at first and the dog ate the clothes. There's a small mound further down the back with a cross at the top – Smudge. Nearby there's another wooden marker. A time capsule containing a letter and a five-cent piece. In a plastic bag. It made sense at the time.

The back was just for garden. Out the front there's a cubby house and a swing. They were used, but not as much as the rusty gate which was big enough for two to swing on. Around the side there's a summer house – or pergola thing. It contains two chairs and a table, and is beyond the view of the house.

Further down the yard there's another shed, never used but often repainted, up to a certain height. Inside the shed there's a black plastic sheet. Big enough to hide Christmas presents. Small enough to be lifted for prying eyes.

It's going to be changed now. They'll rip things up and pull things down. It already looks different. That's OK. It's done its job.

Birth

I'm in labour
With a new world,
One with omens
Scrawled in the sand.

I'm in depression
With an old book,
One with pages
Torn for salvation.

I'm in lust
With a bearded saviour,
One with a bungalow
And weed drying on the shelves.

I'm in remorse
With a wilted iris,
One with a place
With my friend in the ground

I'm in existence
With an obvious scar,
One that is guarded
And revealed only in loss.

Tomorrow with a Stranger

The rain melts the street,
As they cross paths again.
No speech is ordained –
Just a silence screaming jealousy.
They are like the gods:
Trapped in a story that changes
Every time it is told.

Familiar Stranger

I walk into his room
And I am cold.
Smoke spirals up
Enough in an instant
To cloud my perception.

Sit.
Talk.

I make promises
To a Messiah that I'm destined not to honour,
Then beat his intellect
With a shallow embrace.

Flinch.
Weep.

I feel lonely when
We are together;
What makes us so perfect
Is what keeps us apart.

Denial.
Contemplation.

We are
Two halves searching
But our eyes
Never meet.

Chance.
Regret.

Today I think I'll
Tell him I want a voice –
Tomorrow he'll tell me
He's found someone else.

Loss.

New

Present yourself to me
In all your entirety.
Shallow illusions
Declared void.
A mutual existence
Not needing to be explained.
You are not a prophet –
Nor declare to be.
I accept this as a challenge
Displaying intense possibility.

Stomp

The feet march
Within the masses
The faces stop to mourn the earth.
Along the path
Of a golden moon
There's always a dreamer
Who admits his fear.

Mr M

I'm on the run
From the carnival of fun
Instead of the sun,
I'm burning in the moon.
I'm off in his sky
He's getting me high
We're just getting by
With my thoughts of the possible.

Concern

I don't even flinch
At the bitter sensation
Of salt
That drowns my contemplation.
I don't respond
To the insane touch
Of a priest-man on the make.
I don't question
The logic of sanity
Because I know I'll never make it.
I don't love
The brotherhood of discovery
As I am yet to be born.
I don't dream
Of the past –
You know I never meant to hurt you.
I don't pretend
To understand your destiny
I'm just sorry
I made you care.

Haiku

Sir Concrete Jungle
Spends lunchtime with a building,
Screen replacing sun.

Miss Concrete Jungle
Can't get out of the chair –
Stomach wedged in desk.

My Father's Dog Tags

There are two tags – I always wondered why.
Both aluminium, now scratched and dull,
Tightly corded with a leather thong
You must have plaited with your dextrous hands.
Now, I suspect their purpose lay with death,
And when a fated serviceman was killed,
The smaller disc, suspended like frail life,
Was severed from its mate for quick ID
By some officious latter Atropos –
One for the body, the other for the wife.

Inscribed on these two tags was your 'ID'.
Young Jack, naive, enlisting with aplomb
(An added year to fool authorities),
And revelling in the larks at Wagga base.
Then: '15259', alone and lost,
Abandoned at the fall of Singapore.
All semblance of a purpose now quite gone.
Thus reduced, from four letters to five
Numbers—appropriate to mark the change
From man to cipher, as the War ground on.

The dual identity remained with you.
The good mate, kind, gregarious to a fault;
The loving father. Underneath this mask
The man who's scared that life might just implode.
The tags stay with me, comfort somewhat cold
Just tokens of the person now at rest,
Safe from a world that rudely pushed and shoved.
And – just as the tags were never split apart –
Encorded in my being I still hold
My Dad, intact, inviolate; still loved.

On the Wilde Side

For Oscar Wilde the road to Reading Gaol
Began when he embraced his destiny,
And dared to love a man—to scant avail—
And walk the lonely path of honesty.
For him the 'love that dare not speak its name'
—Because the age could not attune to love—
Expressed a nature no-one ought to blame,
Though hypocrites call judgement from above.
But—leaving all the physical aside—
Who could complain at heartfelt tenderness?
Though heartless types this kind of love deride,
Why shouldn't we encourage gentleness?
But Queensberrys still fester everywhere,
And cut off half our scope for human care.

Haiku

Through bedroom window
In limpid moonlight I spy
On gum trees stripping.

    Stringybarks in flower:
    White tentacles, fallen caps.
    Belair in summer snow.

        Re-set your keen clocks
        The ashes' golden leaves say.
        Daylight saving ends.

            Tail-less Mr Skink
            Foreshortened by your sad loss.
            So you've met our cat?

Heading Upstream

for YEM

We are both queer fish
Swimming upstream towards
Spiritual homes which,
Though they may be illusory,
We instinctively seek.

Both fighting against the current
Splashing against the force and flow,
Not noticing that, occasionally,
In attempting a game leap forward
We have plunged into a pool
Further downstream.

As we swim erringly forward
Buffeted by the eddies, currents, whirlpools,
We lose touch with each other
Only to notice, further on,
The glint of sun on straining silver.
And we realise that we are still together
Heading upstream.

The Death of My Uncle

I sit down in the middle of the path.
I don't know why.
The sun shines its usual self:
On the garden, full of flowers
On the paths, freshly swept
On the roof, gutters newly cleaned of leaves.
Nature is indifferent.
Even the cat nuzzling my feet
Is only interested in cadging more food.

I float:
In the middle of nowhere,
Detached.
Out of time. Unconnected.
The death of my uncle brings
Not grief – his life was full –
But loss.
Yet another string is cut from the skein
That moors me to this world.
The tenuous links that connect my fragile self
To this world of other people
Unravel another twist.
'Any man's death diminishes me,' Donne said.
I feel it locally, intimately.

BHH 14 December 1997

Broken Spar

MICHAEL DEVES

Y ou would have wanted to clean the windows. Now I
enjoy the hollowness of a pyrrhic victory: I don't have
to bother about such domestic tidinesses any more.

From where I sit watching through spray-spattered
windows it all seems to happen in slow motion. The long line
of the looping breaker swells up from the small ripples on the
livid green sea, and begins its relentless drive towards the
rocks along the shore. As the perfect curl begins to reach its
head the off-shore gale whips streams of fine spray off the top
and drives it screaming back towards the Antarctic. The wave
ignores this lashing and drives forward, wanting to complete
its circular perfection. Between a couple of sandhills I see a
section of the wave smashed as it breaks its spine on a sub-
merged rock platform. Creamy froth erupts as white suds
surge around the platform, water sucking and cascading in all
directions. The wave barely flinches as the rest of the curl
rolls forward, reaches its apogee and then crashes down with a
menacing explosion of white. When you're up close you feel
the thud of this impact in your solar plexus, feel the lash of salt
spray on the unprotected skin between beanie and jacket. The
wind tugs at your jacket like a beggar hassling you in a slum
street. It's physical.

But in here the sound of the sea coalesces into a sussura-
tion of white noise, penetrated by the occasional dull boom of
another monster wave rebuffed by the rock face. The gale
howls around the windows like unruly banshee spirits
tormenting the edges and angles of the house. As the wind

shifts a few degrees, one of the aluminium windows starts a high-pitched whistle which wanders aimlessly up and down some demonic, tuneless scale. After ten minutes of this mindless cacophony I jam a newspaper edgewise into the window's slide track and mute it. The noise reverts to the crush of the sea.

I'm sitting at the kitchen table. Because this is a holiday house—our favourite holiday house—it's also my work table. The unwashed breakfast dishes still sit disconsolately at one end, my work papers at the other, untended and unproductive. For some reason the sea reminds me of a slow motion replay of a heavy-weight boxing fight. The way you see the arm pull back to load the punch; the humped biceps and the thick twists of rope coiled around the boxer's shoulder and scapula, amassing the energy—and then the release, as, like a well-greased piston, the forearm begins its inevitable, irresistible slide forward. If you know how much strength is stored in a powerful man's muscles, you begin to feel sick in the stomach before the connection. When it comes, the red-tipped ramrod discharges all that horrible energy to perfection. 'Soft' hand meets bony skull. The loose flesh wobbles as the neck muscles, tensed to absorb the shock, give way to the energy wave rolling around the victim's head. Sweat is lashed off in a spray that inevitably sparkles in the bright lights.

As the replay unfolds, it all seems so predictable, so inevitable. Almost *déjà vu*. You can see it coming a mile off, this choreographed cameo.

But it suits my mood to watch.

The breakers form with monotonous inevitability. As they begin their programmed surge there is a measured, Busby Berkeley distance before the next formation, and the next crash. A few torn-off patches of kelp bob ineffectually about, powerless to prevent the fruitless pounding. If you start to think of the forces involved, it's terrifying. At least, you think, it is not a human head trying to play at 'immovable object'. At least, thank God, no brains are going to ricochet around a skull case at the moment of impact.

The rocks around here might disagree. Doorway Rock, a few hundred yards off-shore, has had its innards ripped out by the pounding of the sea. Daylight shows through its eviscerated arch. How 'immovable' is it feeling? How confident of resisting?

The rocks around Robe are geologically soft. Each time a wave smashes itself to smithereens against the cliff faces, it might seem that the rocks have won the battle, but the evidence is otherwise. Over the decade or so since we started coming to Robe large chunks of undermined cliff have given in to the sea. The Obelisk – that comic red-and-white hooped navigation marker from an earlier age of seafaring – is now fenced off on its narrow neck of land, too dangerous for tourists to walk out to. In a few more years the Obelisk, too, will obey and subside. The sea always wins. Occasionally a large chunk of cliff capitulates and – in slow motion? – crashes to the canvas in a spectacular knock-out. But even when the result is not spectacular, the sea still wins: an endless succession of points decisions and TKOs.

Our sparring was only ever mental. But definitely in the welterweight class: quick and deft, but with a reasonable whack from time to time. Not bantamweights, all fast and furious. And certainly not heavyweights, like old philosophers wandering around each other before one lays a grave proposition on the other after due consideration. No. Keen, witty, and occasionally barbed, as a sharpish jibe sails precariously near the truth. Always looking for the points win, and the next bout.

When you finally left me, you went out on a TKO. It certainly wasn't a knock-out, though the result might look the same to the outsider. You would never succumb, never throw in the towel, but you weren't so stupid as to fight senselessly on into the inevitable.

All those years of invisible assault and battery that the body hides inside eventually tally up. All those free radicals and carcinogens were chipping away, invisible to both of us. Slights and bumps becoming slings and arrows. Seemingly shrugged off by the body's ducking and weaving, fending and parrying, until one day, quietly, the oncogene hit its stride. And once it got into gear, the fight became uneven. It gradually took all your strength, and I had to retire from the bout.

I became the trainer, helpless on the sidelines. A bit of verbal encouragement, the occasional swab down between rounds. Increasingly feeble attempts at joshing spars.

Then, finally, I was called in to referee. With the fight becoming one-sided, the only course was to call it off with dignity. I had to go for the TKO. 'Technical knock-out.' Beaten, but not conquered.

So now, I won't clean the windows. I *will* wash the breakfast dishes – in due course – but the windows, no. It's just one small way I can continue our sparring.

Sonneteering

The first few lines seem like they start out well;
The metre works, the thoughts begin to flow –
With any luck they'll build into a swell
And bring to mind some truth you feel you know.
The first quatrain is finished—looking neat!
(Though not a metaphor of any note.)
The rhyme scheme seems too forced, somewhat effete …?
But now the *volta* looms, no time to gloat.
Just these six lines to go and then I'll have
A sonnet to my credit—quite a feat!
And what a thrill that last enjambment gave!
Despite the sight-rhyme, this could be a treat.
But now the couplet strikes! Oh, what a farce!
The thing's not even fit to wipe my arse.

Haiku

My one-eyed monster
It is I who throttle you:
Blood-red motorbike.

The Authors

Tony Bugeja is a a mature age student who is undertaking a major in English literature at Flinders University. He arrived in Adelaide via England, Malta, USA, France and three Australian states. His present interests include short story writing and fighting the wave of racism that threatens this wonderful country. One of Tony's stories written during the creative writing course has been accepted for publication.

Shaun Davis is a graduate from Flinders University with a Bachelor of Arts degree majoring in English and Psychology. He hopes one day to write a novel and entertain people in the same way as his favourite authors have entertained him over the years.

Michael Deves worked in technical publishing for twenty years before returning to university to study literature to make up for accidentally getting a science degree twenty-odd years ago. He is currently working on a doctorate in Australian literature. He has always wanted 'to try his hand' at creative writing; this course has given him the confidence to do so.

Nicole Dickmann is nineteen and studying towards a Bachelor of Arts. She completed the creative writing course – which she enjoyed immensely – to enhance her writing skills and expand her knowledge in all areas of English. She loves writing as way of expressing her thoughts on paper … after all, there is no better way.

Peggy Farrow-Bradley is making a career change to writing, having been an academic in Occupational Therapy for twenty years. Raised in the country until the age thirteen, when she went to boarding school, she became a city dweller. Her goals include becoming a writer, residing in the country and travelling around the world.

Peter Garner resigned from a well-paid, stress-inducing job to do the English, Philosophy and Classics university course that he missed out on when he left school, thirty-odd years ago. He has included writing subjects in his course because he has a strong desire to be a writer, and has already achieved his primary ambition of doing something he enjoys.

Peter Giles was born in Kingscote in 1969 and is now living in Adelaide, far from the pregnant lowing of cattle and the nightly murder of fauna by feral jaws. He now works as a computer systems administrator and programmer.

Jeremy Gill is a thirty-year-old English student in the second year of his Bachelor of Arts. He has been a pizza man, grape picker and has done care work. With such a diverse work history he now feels he is ready to be published.

Annemarie Goodwin is a Law/BA student at Flinders. The creative writing course has given her confidence in approaching publishers, knowing that her work has already been reviewed by other students. Her poetry has been accepted by *The Centoria Literary Magazine*.

D. Stuart Gravestock is a twenty-year-old English and Screen Studies Bachelor of Arts student. He has contributed cartoons, short prose pieces and poems to student publications, and has taken the creative writing course to broaden his publishing options.

Emma   Griffin was born in Alice Springs and completed her Bachelor of Arts at Flinders in 1998. She pursues several active sports, including *tae kwon do* and surfing. Her writing reflects the influence of the horror fiction she reads avidly.

Vanessa Hoare was born in Melbourne in 1975, and in 1985 moved to Adelaide with her family. She is currently undertaking a Bachelor of Education in Upper Primary/Lower Secondary, and aspires to teach in the Carribean. She loves to write and read poetry because it is a rare and honest insight into otherwise unreachable souls.

Beth Jordan was born in 1979 and has grown up to be quite short. She is half-way through a Bachelor of Arts degree in English.

Peter Manthorpe was born in Whyalla and grew up in Adelaide. He has spent about 15 years at sea and is now studying literature – for a change.

Venita Poblocki will complete her Bachelor of Arts this year. She is fascinated by postmodern fiction and was eager to try her hand at the genre.

Kristy Rebbeck is currently in her last year of a Bachelor of Arts degree majoring in English literature. She has always dreamed of becoming an author but has never been in the position to write creatively until this course. She works part time as a photographer, and is now in the process of trying to combine her writing with her photography.

Natasha Samaras is a nineteen-year-old Bachelor of Arts student who is majoring in Greek. She is interested in music and has played the piano for nine years. She intends to become a junior primary teacher as she enjoys working with young children.

Maureen Sexton was born and raised in Perth, and arrived in Adelaide on 1 January 1997. She enjoys large plates of poetry and prose, sprinkled with pepper. She is currently gorging her way through a Bachelor of Arts degree in Writing. She has two adult sons and a profoundly disabled adult daughter. Some of Maureen's poems have now been published.

Gavin Shaw-Ross is from Calgary, Alberta, Canada and is currently in Australia completing his final year of a Bachelor of Community Rehabilitation Degree. He and his wife Tamara, a Masters student in Disability Studies, presently feel most privileged to reside in Port Willunga and drive a Holden Kingswood – something of an Australian cultural icon. They shall soon be returning to Canada where Gavin will write about snow and ice, among other things.

Daniell Sibylla is an idealist, a gardener, a hermit, a sole parent and a poet. She has a driving ambition to change the world – peacefully, poetically and kindly – into something more inclusive and less rigid. Her first true love and her sole inspiration has been her son. Australia is her third country of residence. Her poetry celebrates everyday truths and questions everyday lies.

Brooke Thomas is a student of English and History at Flinders University. Born in Alice Springs and raised in Adelaide, she aspires to write and edit professionally. She finds inspiration for her work in her love of Pacific culture and by reinterpreting the mundane world of student odd-jobs to find the interesting and exotic in everyday life.

Mark Trenwith is an Arts student with a Screen Studies/Drama major. He has written for student films, theatre and radio, and his monologue 'Hare and Tortoise Reunion' has now been recorded by Radio 5UV. He has found the course helpful in exploring different writing forms, and being more objective about his own work.

All the contributors to Fertile Ground *completed the*
Flinders University of South Australia course
'The Craft and Culture of Creative Writing'
in first semester 1998.

Wakefield Press
Box 2266, Kent Town, South Australia 5071
Telephone: (08) 8362 8800 Fax: (08) 8362 7592
www.wakefieldpress.com.au

Wakefield Press thanks Wirra Wirra Vineyards and
Arts South Australia for their continued support.